COMPARATIVE VERTEBRATE ANATOMY

Coleman J. Goin
PROFESSOR OF BIOLOGY
UNIVERSITY OF FLORIDA

Olive B. Goin
UNIVERSITY OF FLORIDA

BARNES & NOBLE, INC.

New York   Publishers & Booksellers   Since 1873

This book is an original work (No. 117) in the original College Outline Series. It was written by distinguished educators, carefully edited,
and produced in accordance with the highest standards of publishing.
The text was set on the Linotype in Caledonia and Spartan by Brown
Brothers, Linotypers, Inc. (New York, N.Y.). The paper for this
edition was manufactured by S. D. Warren Company (Boston, Mass.)
and supplied by Canfield Paper Company (New York, N.Y.). This
edition was printed by General Offset Company (New York, N.Y.) and
bound by Sendor Bindery (New York, N.Y.). The cover was designed
by Rod Lopez-Fabrega.

Preface

This book was written to help the student see the broad span of comparative anatomy.

Oftentimes a student becomes so absorbed in trying to master the numerous details that form a necessary background for an understanding of comparative anatomy that he has difficulty synthesizing from this mass of details the broad picture that he must have if this field is to have real meaning for him. It is our hope that this outline will materially assist him in getting a knowledge of the principles and major concepts of this subject.

The outline summarizes the material usually covered in comparative anatomy courses. The Tabulated Bibliography of Standard Textbooks and the Quick Reference Table permit ready cross-reference between the topics covered in textbooks and the material presented in this outline. Line drawings are used in Chapter 2 to illustrate the major kinds of vertebrates and elsewhere in the book where they can serve as a useful tool in simplifying material that otherwise might require several pages of description.

We are extremely grateful to our colleague, Dr. Frank G. Nordlie, for reading the manuscript in its entirety for factual errors and inconsistencies. To Miss Esther Coogle who made most of the drawings, to Mr. Paul Laessle who prepared a number of additional drawings, and to Mrs. Martha Mitchell who typed the final draft of the manuscript, we owe our thanks.

If this little volume helps the students to see the forest as well as the trees of comparative anatomy, it will have fulfilled its purpose.

About the Authors

Coleman J. Goin is Professor of Biological Sciences at the University of Florida in Gainesville and is a Research Associate at the Carnegie Museum in Pittsburgh, Pennsylvania. He attended the University of Pittsburgh and received the Ph.D. degree from the University of Florida. He is the recipient of research grants from the American Academy of Sciences, the George R. Cooley Fund, and Sigma Xi. In addition to his numerous research articles, Professor Goin wrote *Guide to the Reptiles, Amphibians, and Fresh-Water Fishes of Florida* with A. F. Carr in 1955, and with Mrs. Goin he wrote *Introduction to Herpetology*, published in 1962.

Olive B. Goin received the B.S. degree from Wellesley College and the M.S. degree from the University of Pittsburgh. She has been teaching biology at the University of Florida and has worked in the Laboratory of Mammalogy at the Carnegie Museum. Mrs. Goin wrote *World Outside My Door* which was published in 1955, and is the co-author of *Introduction to Herpetology*.

Table of Contents

Tabulated Bibliography
of Standard Textbooks

This *College Outline* is keyed to standard textbooks in two ways.

1. If you are studying one of the following textbooks consult the cross references here listed to find which pages of the *Outline* summarize the appropriate chapter of your text. (Roman numerals refer to the textbook chapters; Arabic figures to the corresponding pages of this *Outline*.)

2. If you are using the Outline as your basis for study and need a fuller treatment of a topic, consult the pages of any of the standard textbooks as indicated in the Quick Reference Table on pages x–xiii.

Baer, J. G. *Comparative Anatomy of Vertebrates* **(tr. J. Mahon). Butterworths, 1964.**
Sections in this text are not numbered as chapters. The pages here given first refer to pages in the text, those following in parentheses to the pages in this *Outline*.
Pp. 5–21 (1–25); 23–41 (42–54); 43–73 (55–75); 75–77 (81); 79–88 (152–179); 89–107 (180–197); 109–130 (83–95); 131–140 (96–108); 141–152 (131–151); 153–164 (109–130); 165–167 (32–41).

Ballard, W. W. *Comparative Anatomy and Embryology.* **Ronald Press, 1964.**
I (1–8); II (9–25); III (1–8); IV (26–31); V (32–41); VI–XI (32–41); XII (55–75); XIII (180–197); XIV (180–197); XV (180–197); XVI (55–75); XVII (83–95); XVIII (152–179); XIX (42–54); XX (76–82); XXI (76–82); XXII (83–95); XXIII (96–108); XXIV (1–8); XXV (131–151); XXVI (131–151); XXVII (109–120); XXVIII (121–130); XXIX (121–130); XXX (198–206).

Eaton, T. H. Jr. *Comparative Anatomy of the Vertebrates.* **2nd ed. Harper, 1960.**
I (1–8); II (32–41); III (42–54); IV (55–75); V (55–75); VI (76–82); VII (83–108); VIII (131–151); IX (109–130; 198–206); X (180–197); XI (152–179); XII (9–25).

Hyman, L. H. *Comparative Vertebrate Anatomy.* **2nd ed. University of Chicago Press, 1942.**
I (1–8); II (9–28); III (9–25); IV (9–25); V (32–41); VI (42–54); VII (55–75); VIII (55–75); IX (55–75); X (76–82); XI (83–108); XII (131–151); XIII (109–130); XIV (152–197).

Jollie, M. *Chordate Morphology.* **Reinhold, 1962.**
I (9–25); II (9–25); III (55–75); IV (55–75); V (55–75); VI (55–75); VII (32–41); VIII (42–54); IX (96–108); X (109–130); XI (131–151); XII (198–206); XIII (152–179); XIV (76–82); XV (1–8).

Kent, G. C. Jr. *Comparative Anatomy of the Vertebrates.* **Blakiston, 1954.**
I (1–8); II (9–25); III (9–25); IV (32–41); V (42–54); VI (55–75); VII (55–75); VIII (55–75); IX (76–82); X (83–95); XI (96–108); XII

(131–151); XIII (109–130); XIV (152–179); XV (180–197); XVI (198–206).

Leach, W. J. *Functional Anatomy: Mammalian and Comparative.* **3rd ed. McGraw-Hill, 1961.**
I (1–8); II (9–25); III (9–25); IV (55–75); V (42–54); VI (76–82); VII (83–108); VIII (83–95); IX (96–108); X (131–151); XI (109–130); XII (152–179); XIII (180–197); XIV (198–206).

Messer, H. M. *An Introduction to Vertebrate Anatomy.* **Rev. ed. Macmillan, 1947.**
I (1–8); II (1–8; 9–25); III (9–25); IV (9–25); V (32–41); VI (42–54); VII (55–75); VIII (76–82); IX (83–95); X (96–108); XI (131–151); XII (109–120); XIII (121–130); XIV (152–179); XV (180–197); XVI (198–206); XVII (9–25).

Montagna, W. *Comparative Anatomy.* **John Wiley and Sons, 1959.**
I (1–8); II (32–41); III (9–25); IV (42–54); V (55–75); VI (76–82); VII (83–95); VIII (131–151); IX (96–108); X (109–120); XI (121–130); XII (180–197); XIII (152–179); XIV (198–206).

Orr, R. T. *Vertebrate Biology.* **Saunders, 1961.**
I (9–25); II (9–25); III (9–25); IV (9–25); V (9–25); VI (9–25); VII (9–25); XII (121–130); XIII (32–41); XIV (121–130).

Quiring, D. P. *Functional Anatomy of the Vertebrates.* **McGraw-Hill, 1950.**
I (1–8); II (9–25); III (42–54); IV (55–75); V (76–82); VI (152–179); VII (180–197); VIII (83–95); IX (96–108); X (131–151); XI (109–130); XII (198–206); XIII (9–25); XIV (152–179; 198–206).

Rand, H. W. *The Chordates.* **Blakiston, 1950.**
I (1–8); II (83–95); III (131–151); IV (109–130); V (55–82); VI (198–206); VII (121–130); VIII (26–31); XI (9–25); XII (9–25); XIII (9–25); XIV (9–25); XV (9–25); XVI (42–82); XVII (83–151); XVIII (152–179); XIX (9–25).

Romer, A. S. *The Vertebrate Body.* **3rd ed. Saunders, 1962.**
I (1–8); II (9–25); III (9–25); IV (26–31); V (32–41); VI (42–54); VII (55–75); VIII (55–75); IX (76–82); X (83–108); XI (96–108); XII (83–95); XIII (109–130); XIV (131–151); XV (180–197); XVI (152–179); XVII (198–206).

Romer, A. S. *The Vertebrate Body (Shorter Version).* **3rd ed. Saunders, 1962.**
I (1–8); II (9–25); III (9–25); IV (26–31); V (32–41); VI (42–54); VII (55–75); VIII (57–63); IX (76–82); X (83–108); XI (96–108); XII (83–95); XIII (109–130); XIV (131–151); XV (180–197); XVI (152–179); XVII (198–206).

Smith, H. M. *Evolution of Chordate Structure.* **Holt, Rinehart and Winston, 1960.**
I (1–8); II (9–25); III (9–25); IV (32–41); V (42–54); VI (55–75); VII (55–75); VIII (55–75); IX (76–82); X (83–108); XI (83–108); XII (198–206); XIII (109–130); XIV (131–151); XV (180–197); XVI (152–179).

Torrey, T. W. *Morphogenesis of the Vertebrates.* **John Wiley and Sons, 1962.**
I (9–25); II (9–25); III (32–41); IV–X (32–41); XI (42–54); XII (55–75); XIII (76–82); XIV (83–95); XV (83–108); XVI (109–130); XVII (131–151); XVIII (152–197).

Walter, H. E., and Sayles, L. P. *Biology of the Vertebrates.* **3rd ed. Macmillan, 1949.**
I (1–8); II (9–25); III (9–25); IV (9–25); V (9–25); VI (26–31); VII (26–31); VIII (32–41); X (42–54); XI (83–95); XII (131–151); XIII (96–108); XIV (109–120); XV (121–130); XVI (198–206); XVII (55–75); XVIII (76–82); XIX (152–179); XX (180–197).

Weichert, C. K. *Anatomy of the Chordates.* **2nd ed. McGraw-Hill, 1958.**
I (1–8); II (9–25); III (32–41); IV (42–54); V (83–95); VI (96–108); VII (109–120); VIII (121–130); IX (198–206); X (55–75); XI (76–82); XII (131–151); XIII (152–179); XIV (180–197).

Weichert, C. K. *Elements of Chordate Anatomy.* **2nd ed. McGraw-Hill, 1959.**
I (1–8); II (9–25); III (26–31); IV (42–54); V (83–95); VI (96–108); VII (109–120); VIII (121–130); IX (198–206); X (55–75); XI (76–82); XII (131–151); XIII (152–179); XIV (180–197); XV (207–214).

Young, J. Z. *The Life of Vertebrates.* **2nd ed. Oxford University Press, 1962.**
This book is arranged by the groups of animals; under each group the embryology and the structure of the various systems are discussed.

Quick Reference Table

See preceding pages

Quick Reference Table

See preceding pages

to Standard Textbooks (Continued)

for complete titles.

Romer Shorter	Smith	Torrey	Walter & Sayles	Weichert	Weichert Elements	Young
1–29	1–50	16–19	3–12	1–10	1–6	1–41
31–79	51–68	19–41	13–80	11–49	7–47	through-out
80–87		through-out	129–155			
88–111	69–92	through-out	156–181	50–89	48–67	41–46
112–122	93–126	179–211	195–260	90–140	68–103	through-out
123–197 233–243	127–222	212–285 324–329	517–641	366–462	230–297	through-out
198–228	223–249	286–313	642–664	463–496	298–322	through-out
260–275	260–309	314–324 344–349 395–396	261–328	141–186	104–134	through-out
229–259	260–309	329–342	382–426	187–238	135–167	through-out
276–290	313–347	362–378 396	427–446	239–260	168–181	through-out
290–307	313–347	378–405	447–496	261–318	182–210	through-out
308–340	348–396	407–469	329–381	497–556	323–368	through-out
368–406	447–492	470–531	665–752	557–619	369–407	through-out
341–367	397–446	531–562	753–832	620–682	408–443	through-out
407–419	310–312	342–344	497–516	319–365	211–229	through-out
421–427				846–856	444–456	
428–441	493–502	563–581				

1

Introduction

The study of vertebrate anatomy offers particularly rich opportunities to the student of today. It gives him a direct acquaintance with many of the important principles and theories of biology, and introduces him to the structure, function, and evolutionary pattern of the group of animals that holds the greatest interest for him, since he himself belongs to it. Study of this subject gives the potential medical student a background in the evolution of the structures that comprise the human body, and hence not only a firsthand experience in learning the parts of the vertebrate body but also an understanding of why man is as he is.

PHYLUM CHORDATA

The vertebrates belong to the phylum Chordata, a major group of animals that differ from all others by the possession at some stage in the life cycle of the following combination of characters: (1) a hollow, dorsal nerve cord; (2) a stiffening rod, or notochord, down the back; and (3) pharyngeal slits which frequently bear gills. Several subphyla in addition to the vertebrates are generally recognized within the phylum Chordata. While these groups are not usually studied in the comparative anatomy laboratory, the student should become familiar with them simply because he will then have a better understanding of the place of the vertebrates in nature.

Subphylum Hemichordata. This group includes the acorn worms, which are worm-shaped burrowers with well developed gill structures used primarily for food-gathering. A dorsal, more or less hollow nerve strand may be homologous with the vertebrate dorsal nerve cord. Also included in the hemichordates are

1

the pterobranchs—simple, sessile animals somewhat like plants in appearance—which gather food by ciliated, branching, tentacle-like structures called *lophophores*. The animals in this subphylum show little or no trace of the development of a notochord. They are placed in the Chordata largely because of their pharyngeal gill slits, but many authorities consider them a distinct, though related, phylum.

FIG. 1-1. A representative of the Hemichordata, *Balanoglossus,* an acorn worm.

Subphylum Urochordata (Tunicata). The adult tunicates are sessile or floating organisms whose chief chordate character is a well developed pharyngeal gill apparatus. Many of them, though, pass through a free-swimming larval stage in which both a notochord and a hollow, dorsal nerve cord are present.

Subphylum Cephalochordata. These little marine animals, of which amphioxus is a familiar example, have a well developed notochord, a dorsal, hollow nerve cord, and a well developed gill apparatus. Amphioxus looks more like a vertebrate than do the members of the two preceding subphyla. Superficially, it resembles a small fish, though it lacks paired fins. (See Fig. 1-3.)

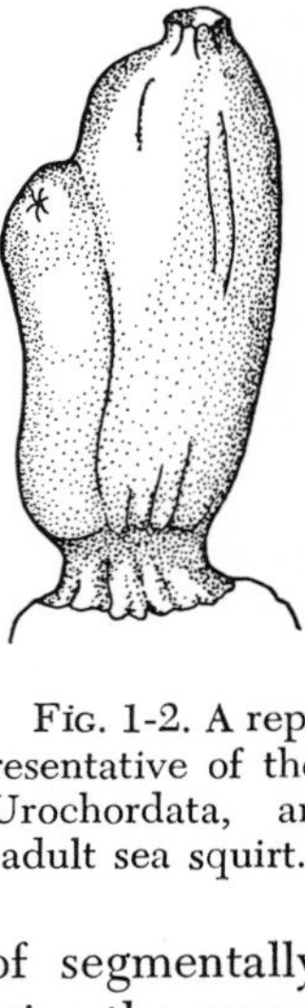

Subphylum Vertebrata. To this subphylum belong the animals with which we will be concerned. In addition to the characters mentioned above for members of the phylum Chordata, the vertebrates possess a backbone of segmentally arranged skeletal structures, the *vertebrae,* which give the group its name.

FIG. 1-2. A representative of the Urochordata, an adult sea squirt.

THE FOUR MAJOR VERTEBRATE CHARACTERISTICS

There are four major characteristics which set the vertebrates apart from all other animals and which, in combination, serve to identify any vertebrate as a member of this particular subphylum. These traits are: (1) the embryonic development of a notochord; (2) the presence of a hollow, dorsal nerve cord; (3) the presence of a pharynx with slits in its wall; and (4) the development of bony or cartilaginous vertebral blocks. The hagfish is exceptional in that it lacks vertebrae.

FIG. 1-3. A representative of the Cephalochordata, Amphioxus, *Branchiostoma*.

Notochord. The notochord, the structure that gives the phylum Chordata its name, is the primitive, supporting endoskeletal element of the vertebrates. It is a longitudinally placed, flexible, axial rod composed of connective tissue. This structure lies dorsal to the alimentary canal, ventral to the nerve cord, and generally extends from the level of the midbrain to the tip of the tail. It is present in every vertebrate embryo.

Hollow, Dorsal Nerve Cord. You may perhaps recall that the central nervous system in such forms as earthworms and grasshoppers consists primarily of longitudinal nerve trunks which lie ventral to the alimentary canal. This condition contrasts sharply with that of the vertebrates, in which the central nervous system is always a single, hollow, tubelike structure lying dorsal to the notochord. Anteriorly, it is somewhat enlarged to form the brain. From this central brain and nerve cord, nerves pass to other structures of the body.

Pharyngeal Slits. The pharynx is a muscular tube associated primarily with feeding. It connects the mouth with the esophagus. In the vertebrates, the pharynx is perforated along each side by a series of slits. There may be numerous slits or only a single, semi-enclosed pair—the middle ear cavities of the higher vertebrates. Even if the slits are closed, however, the pouches from which they were originally formed are of some importance, for they may differentiate into such organs as the tonsils and certain endocrine glands.

Vertebrae. A vertebral column is a salient characteristic of the vertebrates. It is present in each member of this subphylum, with the single exception of the hagfishes in which it is not developed. (However, since the hagfishes are obviously closely related to the lampreys, which do have vertebral structures, we include them among the animals of this subphylum.) The vertebrae may be nothing more than a series of little cartilaginous blocks lying alongside the notochord, or they may be well ossified, extremely complex structures such as the individual units of the backbone of man.

THE VERTEBRATE BODY PLAN

In addition to the characters given above, the vertebrates share a basic similarity of body plan.

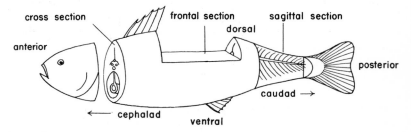

Fig. 1-4. Directions and planes in a vertebrate body.

Bilateral Symmetry and Body Planes. The vertebrates have three body axes: (1) an anteroposterior or longitudinal axis, running from the anterior or head end to the posterior or tail end; (2) a dorsoventral axis, running from the dorsal (back) side to the ventral side; and (3) a left-right axis from the left to the right side of the body. The structures found at one end of both the anteroposterior axis and the dorsoventral axis are strikingly different from those found at the other end, whereas the third, or left-right axis, has essentially identical structures present on each side; the left side of the body is a mirror image of the right. When only one of the body axes has similar structures on either side, the condition is known as *bilateral symmetry*.

In discussing the vertebrate body, it is often convenient to locate the parts of the body in relation to three major series of planes. A *transverse plane* is one that divides the body into anterior and posterior parts. A *sagittal plane* divides the body into right and left parts. A *frontal plane* divides the body into dorsal and ventral parts. A cut along a transverse plane is called a *cross section*; a cut along a sagittal plane is a *sagittal section;* and a cut along a frontal plane is a *frontal section* (Fig. 1-4).

Regions of the Vertebrate Body. The vertebrate body is typically divided into three primary regions: head, trunk, and tail. All but a few vertebrates have paired appendages associated with the trunk region, and the higher vertebrate groups have a neck placed between the head and the trunk.

Head. Cephalization, the concentration of structures in the head region, is shown in its most advanced state among the vertebrates. Not only is there a concentration of tissue of the central nervous system, or brain, in the head region, but correlated with this are increased concentrations of the sense organs and of protective skeletal coverings for the brain. The mouth, with its associated jaws (if present), and the openings of the respiratory system are also located in this end of the body.

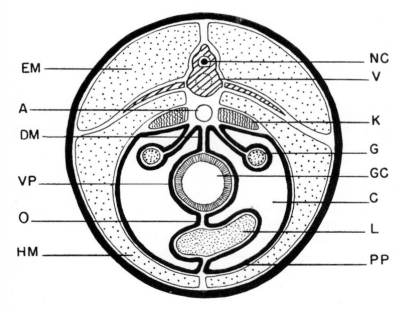

Fig. 1-5. Hypothetical cross section through the trunk of a typical vertebrate, showing relationship of structures and organs. EM, epaxial muscles; A, dorsal aorta; DM, dorsal mesentery; VP, visceral peritoneum; O, omentum; HM, hypaxial muscles; NC, nerve cord; V, vertebra; K, kidney; G, gonad; GC, gut cavity; C, coelom; L, liver; PP, parietal peritoneum.

Trunk. The great majority of the internal organs, or *viscera,* are located in the trunk region. The trunk is essentially a double hollow tube. The outer part of the tube forms the body wall and the inner part forms the digestive tract. The space between them is the body cavity, or *coelom.* The surface lining of the coelom is the *parietal peritoneum.* The viscera either lie against the wall of the coelom or they are suspended in it; they are surrounded by the *visceral peritoneum. Mesenteries* are sheets of peritoneum by which the viscera are suspended in the coelom.

The heart lies in a separate portion of the coelomic cavity, the *pericardial cavity.* The lungs, when present, usually lie in the coelomic cavity proper. Mammals, however, have a sheet of muscular tissue, the *diaphragm,* which separates the body cavity into the *peritoneal cavity* and the paired *pleural cavities* which contain the lungs.

Some organs, such as the kidneys, sometimes lie between the peritoneum and the body wall proper and are then said to be *retroperitoneal.* The body cavities also contain large blood vessels, certain glands, and other soft parts. The trunk region is generally considered to extend posteriorly to the posterior margin of the opening of the *cloaca* or of the *anus.*

The neck, when it is present, is an anterior elongation of the trunk region. It is found only in the reptiles, birds, and mammals.

Tail. The tail is a posterior appendage primitively associated with locomotion, although it may develop such secondary functions as food storage, protection, support, etc. There is a great deal of variation in the tail among vertebrates. In some it is extremely short, while in others it is quite long and may be very useful. Some of the monkeys, for example, use it as a prehensile organ in climbing. The porcupine uses it as a weapon of defense. In most aquatic vertebrates, the tail is still primarily an organ of locomotion. Man has a tail in early embryonic life, and vestiges of it may be seen in the last, or *caudal,* series of vertebrae of the human skeleton.

Appendages. Sometimes we divide the subphylum Vertebrata into two superclasses, Tetrapoda and Pisces, depending on whether or not the animals have paired limbs which are basically similar structurally to those of man. The lowest vertebrates (cyclostomes) lack any paired appendages at all, but most fishes and fishlike vertebrates have two pairs of appendages (pectoral fins and pelvic fins) in which the supporting elements are horny rays. Beginning with the amphibians, we find the development of two pairs of limbs (pectoral and pelvic) in which the supporting skeletal elements are more or less modified from a basic *pentadactyl* (five-digit) plan. The pentadactyl limb is also known as the *tetrapod* (four-foot) limb. The anterior pair may be legs, wings, or flippers. The posterior pair are usually either legs or flippers. Occasionally, one or both pairs have been lost entirely.

STRUCTURE OF THE VERTEBRATE BODY

As in all animals, the basic unit of the vertebrate body is the cell. Cells that are similar in function and structure are arranged in groups so that they work together; such groups of cells are known as *tissues*. Thus we have connective tissue, muscular tissue, nervous tissue, etc. (see Chap. 3). Tissues of various sorts are organized together into structures which perform particular body functions; these localized groups of tissues having specific functions are known as *organs*. For example, the heart is an organ, the liver is an organ, the kidney is an organ. Furthermore, various groups of organs work together for a common purpose and for the common welfare of the body. An arrangement of organs into such a functional unit we call a *system*. The number of systems recognized varies somewhat from one textbook to another, but, in general, most workers acknowledge about ten or eleven systems. They are as follows:

Integumentary System. This system includes the skin and all of its various derivatives. It serves to cover and protect the body and may have such secondary functions as heat control, locomotion, food storage, or others. It is the part of the body that is directly exposed to the external environment.

Skeletal System. The skeletal system is used for support of the body, often for protection (particularly in the brain region), and, since the various parts of it are movable in relation to each other, for locomotion. The skeleton also has a secondary function in relation to blood cell production.

Muscular System. This is the system of the body that has to do with motion. The muscles contract and by the resultant pull move the body or its various parts. In addition to the primary function of producing motion, the muscles may also play a part in heat production and in the protection of soft parts which may be buried well below the superficial muscles.

Digestive System. The digestive system functions in the ingestion of food and its modification into substances that can enter the cells of the body and be used by them. In adults of all vertebrates, the digestive system is, without exception, essentially a tube having an anterior opening, or *mouth,* and a posterior opening, the *vent* or the *anus.*

Respiratory System. The respiratory system brings about the exchange of gases between the animal and its environment. It functions to provide oxygen for the animal's body and to remove carbon dioxide from it.

Excretory System. This system has the function of excretion, or the removal of nitrogenous wastes from the body. It also serves to regulate the salt and water content of the body.

Reproductive System. This is the system that is concerned with the production of a new generation; it thus differs from the other systems which have to do with the maintenance of the individual.

Circulatory System. The circulatory system is the transport mechanism of the body. All the other systems depend on it to carry to them, or to take away, food, gases, waste products, heat, and chemical secretions.

Nervous System. The nervous system has to do primarily with the co-ordination of body activities. It is through the nervous system that we receive stimuli from the outside world and co-ordinate our body activities accordingly.

Sensory Receptors. The various structures (eye, ear, etc.) through which we receive stimuli from outside are sometimes set apart from the nervous system, largely as a matter of convenience, although all of them do involve nervous tissue.

Endocrine System. This system comprises a group of glands that have the function of co-ordinating different body activities with one another. Thus, it is through hormones, the chemicals secreted by these glands, that the muscular system is co-ordinated with the respiratory system, and that in turn with the digestive system.

2

The Vertebrate Classes

The subphylum Vertebrata includes the vast majority of the chordates. The spinal cord is protected by the vertebrae, a series of skeletal elements which develop in association with the notochord. The notochord is for the most part replaced by the vertebrae in adult tetrapods. All vertebrates have the anterior end of the nerve cord expanded to form a brain, which is protected by a cartilaginous or bony box, the cranium. The subphylum is divided into eight classes.

CLASS AGNATHA

These are the most primitive of the vertebrates. The group is rather widely distributed but there are relatively few living species.

Characters of Agnatha. As the name indicates, the Agnatha are without jaws. The mouth is round and, in the modern forms at least, armed with a raspin.g, tongue-like structure. The Agnatha lack true paired fins, though some of the fossil forms had lateral projections from the body that probably served the same functions of balancing and steering.

Orders of Agnatha. Several orders of extinct forms are known collectively as *ostracoderms*. They were armored with bony plates and some had internal skeletons of bone. The modern Agnatha are placed in the order *Cyclostomata*. They are round-bodied, eel-like animals without scales. There is only a single nasal sac. The skeleton is entirely cartilaginous. The cyclostomes are divided into two suborders: Myxinoidea, the hagfishes; and Petromyzontia, the lampreys. The lampreys are marine or fresh-water forms in which the mouth is surrounded by a sucking disk, rudi-

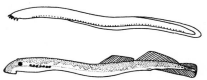

FIG. 2-1. Representative agnathans. Top: the Atlantic hagfish, *Myxine*. Bottom: the sea lamprey, *Petromyzon*.

ments of vertebrae are present, and there are seven pairs of gill slits. The adults may be external parasites on fish, attaching themselves to their host by means of the sucking disk. The hagfishes are marine and are internal parasites on fish. They lack the sucking disk and vertebrae, and have from six to fourteen gill slits. (Fig. 2-1.)

CLASS PLACODERMI

The grotesque, armored placoderms, which probably evolved from the ostracoderms, are now all extinct. The placoderms developed primitive jaws and paired fins. The body was more or less covered by a well developed, bony armor of scales or large plates. (Fig. 2-2.)

CLASS CHONDRICHTHYES

The sharks and their allies evolved from placoderms or placoderm-like forms and are still an abundant and flourishing group in the seas of the world.

Characters of Chondrichthyes. The skeleton is entirely cartilaginous, although the Chondrichthyes are believed to have descended from ancestors that did form true bone. Sharks have well developed jaws and paired fins. The heart is two-chambered. The scales are placoid, each consisting of a bony plate embedded in the dermis of the skin, from which a spine of dentine projects outward through the epidermis. Either the young are born alive, or the eggs when laid are encased in an elaborate, horny shell. The eggs must therefore be fertilized within the body of the female. Male sharks have projections from the median portions of the pelvic fins, the *claspers*, by which the sperm are transmitted to the cloaca of the female.

Orders of Chondrichthyes. There are two living orders of Chondrichthyes.

Order *Elasmobranchii* (*Selachii*). These are the typical sharks (suborder Squali) and the skates and rays (suborder Batoidea).

They lack an *operculum,* the covering of the gill chamber found in higher fishes, so that the gill slits are exposed. The first pharyngeal slit is usually modified to form a round opening, the *spiracle.* The upper jaw is not fused to the skull, but is loosely attached to it by the hyomandibular cartilage—a *hyostylic jaw.*

Squalus acanthias, the spiny dogfish, is an example of Elasmobranchii.

Order Holocephali. The chimeras are rather rare, oceanic forms. An operculum is present, but it is simply a flap of skin, not bony as in the higher fishes. There is no spiracle and the vertebrae are poorly developed. The upper jaw is fused to the skull—an *autostylic jaw.* (Fig. 2-2.)

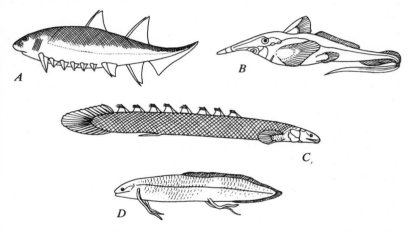

FIG. 2-2. Examples of the fishes. *A,* a representative placoderm, the acanthodian or "spiny shark"; *B,* a holocephalian, the chimera (*Chimaera*); *C,* a chondrostean, the bichir of the Nile River (*Polypterus*); *D,* a representative of the Dipnoi, the African lungfish (*Protopterus*).

CLASS OSTEICHTHYES

The great majority of the fishes of the world belong to the class of bony fishes.

Characters of Osteichthyes. The skeletons of these forms contain bone. Some of the bones of the skull are *dermal bones,* derived from bony plates of the ancestral fishes, which have sunk down to become part of the internal skeleton. The operculum is also bony. Except in the dipnoans, the heart is two-chambered.

The majority of bony fishes have external fertilization. In a few forms, however, the young are born alive and these fish necessarily have internal fertilization. The intromittent organ of such fish is formed by an elongation of the anterior border of the anal fin and is not homologous with the claspers of the sharks.

Subclasses of Osteichthyes. At their first appearance in the fossil record in the early Devonian period, the Osteichthyes were already divided into two major groups.

Subclass Actinopterygii. The ray-finned fishes are the dominant fishes of the world today. In them the paired fins are webs of skin supported by horny rays. There is no internal nostril; the external nostril leads into a blind nasal sac quite unconnected with the mouth. The jaw is hyostylic. The Actinopterygii are divided into three superorders.

SUPERORDER CHONDROSTEI. These are the most primitive of the ray-finned fishes. The endoskelton of modern chondrosteans is largely cartilaginous. Scales, when present, are of the *ganoid* type; that is, the outer portion is composed of layers of a hard, shiny, translucent material called *ganoin*. A spiracle is present. Only a few Chondrostei survive today. (Fig. 2-2.)

SUPERORDER HOLOSTEI. Like the Chondrostei, the holosteans are represented today by only a few members, but they once were the dominant fishes. The skeleton is largely bony rather than cartilaginous. The scales may lose their ganoid covering, but at least some of the scales are of the ganoid type. The spiracle is absent.

The bowfin, *Amia calva,* is an example of the Holostei.

SUPERORDER TELEOSTEI. The remaining actinopterygians are all included in one very large superorder. The skeleton is well ossified. The scales lack ganoin and are either *cycloid* (rounded) or *ctenoid* (with the free edge bearing numerous comblike projections). There is no spiracle. About 20,000 different kinds of teleosts survive today; they are divided into a large number of orders. Among the more important orders are: Isospondyli (herring, trout, salmon, etc.); Ostariophysi (catfishes, carp, etc.); and Percomorphi (perch, mackerel, mullet, etc.).

Subclass Choanichthyes (Sarcopterygii). Although the Choanichthyes are represented by very few forms today, they are of major evolutionary importance, since it was from them that the terrestrial vertebrates evolved. The nasal cavities have two sets of openings, one pair opening to the outside, the *external nares*, and one pair opening into the mouth, the *internal nares* or *choanae*, which give the group its name. Lungs, primitive vertebrate structures which in the teleosts have been converted into a swim bladder, are present. The heart is three-chambered. The paired fins are fleshy, not membranous as in the actinopterygians, and are supported by bony elements rather than by horny rays. The subclass is divided into two orders.

ORDER DIPNOI. The three living genera of lungfishes are found in the tropics (one in Africa, one in South America, and one in Australia). They live in regions of seasonal drought and are able to survive in stagnant waters by breathing air. When the water holes dry up completely, the African and South American forms aestivate in burrows in the mud, where they can survive for months without water. The skeleton is little ossified in the dipnoans. They have specialized, fan-shaped tooth-plates formed by the fusion of once discrete, conical teeth. (Fig. 2-2.)

ORDER CROSSOPTERYGII. This is the group from which the amphibians arose. Common in the Devonian, the order is represented today by a single, aberrant, marine form. The skelton is better ossified than in the dipnoans, and the teeth are sharp, pointed structures, not modified into crushing plates.

Latimeria, the coelacanth, is an example of Crossopterygii.

CLASS AMPHIBIA

Amphibians were the first vertebrates to move out on land. They are also the first of the tetrapod classes, those that have paired limbs with digits instead of fins. (A few amphibians lack one or both pairs of limbs.)

Characters of Amphibia. Amphibians have soft, glandular skins, usually without scales. Methods of respiration vary; most adults have lungs, but a few retain the gills of the larvae. The skin is important in respiration and in some is the chief respiratory organ. The heart is three-chambered. The eggs lack a shell and are usually laid in water, and the young generally pass through a free-swimming, larval stage before metamorphosing into the adult form.

Superorders of Amphibia.[1] The amphibians are divided into four superorders, two with living representatives.

Superorder Lepospondyli. These are mostly small amphibians with slender bodies and with limbs reduced or absent. The superorder includes several extinct orders and three living ones.

ORDER TRACHYSTOMATA. These are eel-shaped, aquatic animals with the fore limbs reduced and the hind limbs absent. They never metamorphose, but retain the gills and other larval characters throughout life. The trachystomes are included in the Caudata in most comparative anatomy texts, but recent research indicates the two are descended from quite distinct fossil groups. The order includes only two living genera, *Siren* and *Pseudobranchus,* found only in southeastern United States and northeastern Mexico.

ORDER CAUDATA (URODELA). The modern salamanders are mostly small animals, with long, slim bodies and tails, and feeble legs. There is a strong tendency toward reduction in the bones of the skull. The primitive forms have external fertilization, but more advanced salamanders practice internal fertilization by means of a packet of sperm deposited by the male and picked up by the female—a method unique among the vertebrates. A few salamanders are entirely terrestrial, but most must return to the water to breed, and some are entirely aquatic, retaining many of the

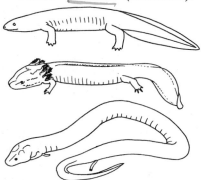

FIG. 2-3. Representative salamanders of the order Caudata. Top: the newt, *Diemictylus.* Middle: the mudpuppy, *Necturus.* Bottom: the Congo eel, *Amphiuma.*

[1] The terms "Stegocephalia" and "Labyrinthodontia" frequently appear in amphibian classifications. Stegocephalia was a "wastepaper basket" grouping of all pre-Jurassic amphibians which now have been shown to represent a number of very different phyletic lines. Labyrinthodontia included the fossil groups Temnospondyli and Anthracosauria. Recent research indicates, however, that the anthracosaurs are closer to the Salientia, and perhaps to the Lepospondyli, than they are to the Temnospondyls. There seems no good reason, then, for continuing to lump them together.

larval characteristics as adults. The order includes about 300 living species. (Fig. 2-3.)

ORDER APODA. The caecilians are worm-like, burrowing amphibians, without limbs or limb girdles, and with reduced tails. The more primitive genera have tiny dermal scales embedded in the skin. Fertilization is internal, and the males have a copulatory organ formed from a modified portion of the cloaca. The eggs are laid on land. The young may hatch either before or after metamorphosis. A

FIG. 2-4. A representative of the Apoda, the caecilian (*Ichthyophis*), coiled around eggs.

few caecilians are live-bearers. This is a small order, with less than 100 living species, all found in the tropics.

Superorder Salientia. The frogs have the hind legs more or less elongated and specialized for jumping. They lack tails, and the caudal vertebrae are replaced by a long, rod-shaped structure, the *urostyle*. In all but a few frogs, fertilization is external and the eggs are usually, though not always, laid in water. Some frogs are quite aquatic, though none fails to complete metamorphosis; others are well adapted to life on land. This is the most successful group of living amphibians, with about 1,800 living species, all of which are included in the Order Anura.

Superorders Temnospondyli and Anthracosauria. The extinct amphibians include the temnospondyls which are the stem amphibians that evolved from the crossopterygians in the Devonian Period, and the anthracosaurs, which gave rise to the reptiles. The early members of both groups were still largely aquatic, but were probably able to crawl out on land. Many of the later temnospondyls and anthracosaurs were quite terrestrial, stout-bodied animals, larger than most modern amphibians. *Pteroplax,* an anthracosaur, reached an estimated length of 15 feet (450 cm.).

Ichthyostega, the earliest temnospondyl, and *Seymouria,* a close relative of the ancestor of the reptiles, are examples of Temnospondyli and Anthracosauria.

CLASS REPTILIA

As a group, the reptiles are the first completely terrestrial vertebrates, though some have become secondarily aquatic and, as was pointed out above, there are a few amphibians which no longer need to return to the water to breed.

Characters of Reptilia. Like the lower vertebrates, and unlike the birds and mammals, reptiles are *ectothermic;* that is, their body temperature is largely controlled by factors in the external environment.[2] They are more or less covered with scales which develop from the epidermal layer of the skin, not from the dermal layer, as do the scales of fishes. The heart is three-chambered (except in the crocodilians) and lungs are always present. Fertilization is always internal in the reptiles and they either lay eggs or bear live young. The egg is surrounded by a leathery or calcareous shell and is always laid on land. The developing embryo is enclosed in a fluid-filled space surrounded by a membrane, the *amnion.* This character the reptiles share with the birds and mammals; these three groups, therefore, are known collectively as the *amniotes.* There is never an aquatic larval stage. Most modern reptiles are fairly small animals, but some of the extinct dinosaurs were enormous, the largest terrestrial animals ever evolved.

Subclasses of Reptilia. The reptiles are divided into six subclasses, three with living members.

Subclass Anapsida. These are reptiles in which the roof of the skull has no openings in the temporal region. The subclass includes both the extinct order Cotylosauria, the primitive stem reptiles, and the order Testudinata (Chelonia), to which the modern turtles belong. Turtles have a protective shell formed by a fusion of bony dermal plates with underlying skeletal parts (the ribs, vertebrae, and girdles); usually the shell is covered by horny epidermal scales. Most turtles live in aquatic habitats and some have become entirely marine, but all must return to land to lay their eggs. About 300 species of testudinates survive today. (Fig. 2-5.)

Subclass Lepidosauria. These reptiles have basically two openings in the temporal region of the skull roof, though in most of the later forms one or both of the arches of bone delimiting the

---

[2] The ectothermic vertebrates are frequently referred to as *poikilotherms.* "Poikilothermic" means having a variable body temperature. Reptiles absorb heat from the environment, but most of them, when active, maintain a rather constant body temperature through behavioral means, regardless of changes in the environmental temperature.

openings have been lost, thereby obscuring the double nature of the openings. Two living orders and one extinct one (Eosuchia) are included.

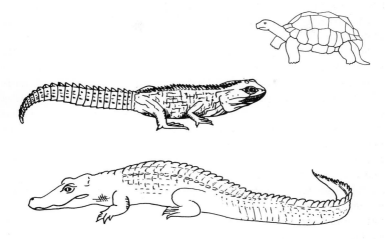

Fig. 2-5. Representative reptiles. Top: an anapsid, the tortoise (*Testudo*). Middle: the rhynchocephalian, tuatara (*Sphenodon punctatum*). Bottom: an archosaur, the alligator (*Alligator mississippiensis*).

ORDER RHYNCHOCEPHALIA. The beak-headed reptiles are represented today by a single species, the tuatara, which is found only on a few islands off the coast of New Zealand. The tuatara is lizard-like in appearance and lethargic in behavior. There is a well developed third eye in the center of the forehead and both temporal arches are present. Although the tuatara lacks a copulatory organ, fertilization is internal. The eggs are laid in a shallow hole dug by the female and take thirteen months to hatch. (Fig. 2-5.)

ORDER SQUAMATA. This order includes the lizards and snakes, and is the most numerous, widespread, and diverse—in a word, the most successful—order of living reptiles. In contrast to the rhynchocephalians, the squamates have lost one or both of the temporal arches. They have paired copulatory organs, the *hemipenes*. There are two living suborders.

Suborder Lacertilia (*Sauria*). Most lizards have two pairs of limbs, though sometimes one or both pairs have been lost. Usually lizards have visible external ear openings and movable eyelids. The two halves of the lower jaw are firmly united so that lizards cannot open their mouths as widely as the snakes can. Most lizards lay eggs, but some bear living young. About 3,000 living species of lizards are known.

The collared lizard, *Crotophytus collaris,* is a representative of Lacertilia.

Suborder Serpentes (*Ophidia*). Snakes are elongated, usually legless animals, though a few have vestigial limbs and limb girdles. They lack a sternum and external ear openings. The eyelids of most snakes are fused and transparent. Usually the two halves of the lower jaw are not fused and the bones of the facial region are loosely joined to each other and to the cranium. Because of this, snakes have a wide gape and can engulf large prey. Snakes occupy a wide variety of habitats, from deserts to lakes and oceans, and from burrows underground to tall trees. Like the lizards, they may be either oviparous or ovoviviparous. There are about 2,700 species of snakes living today.

Subclass Archosauria. Represented today only by the crocodilians, the archosaurs were the ruling reptiles of the Mesozoic era. The subclass includes the dinosaurs, the flying reptiles (Pterosauria), and also the ancestors of the birds. Like the lepidosaurs, the archosaurs have two temporal openings in the skull roof. There is a strong tendency toward the development of bipedalism in the group.

ORDER CROCODILIA (LORICATA). The crocodilians are in many ways the most advanced of the living reptiles. The heart is four-chambered, not three-chambered as it is in other living reptiles. A hard palate has formed in the roof of the mouth, separating it into oral and nasal cavities. The teeth are set in sockets in the jawbone, not perched on top of it. The 21 living species of crocodilians are all largely aquatic. Most live in the tropics, though a few are found in warm temperate regions. All crocodilians lay eggs which they bury either in a nest of trash or in a mound of sand heaped up by the mother. (Fig. 2-5.)

EXTINCT ORDERS OF ARCHOSAURIA. Order Thecondontia includes the primitive ancestral archosaurs, as well as the crocodile-like phytosaurs. Order Pterosauria includes the flying reptiles. Their flight mechanism resembled that of a bat rather than that of a bird; it consisted of a membrane of skin stretched between the front and hind limbs. In the pterosaurs an elongated fourth finger supported this membrane, but in the bats the last four fingers support it.

The large and heterogeneous assemblage of animals known as dinosaurs are placed in two orders: Saurischia and Ornithischia. Some were active, bipedal carnivores; others were lumbering, quadrupedal herbivores. Not all were gigantic—some were little larger than a barnyard chicken.

Tyrannosaurus rex, the King of the Carnivores, is a representative member of Archosauria.

Subclasses Ichthyopterygia, Synaptosauria (Euryapsida), and Synapsida. The members of these subclasses are all extinct. The first two left no descendants, but the Synapsida gave rise to the mammals.

Cynognathus, a mammal-like reptile, is an example of Synapsida.

CLASS AVES

Descendants of the archosaurs, the birds are sometimes called "glorified reptiles." Most of the characters by which they differ from the reptiles are adaptations for flight. They are a numerous and highly successful group; about 9,000 different species of living birds have been described, a greater number than for any other tetrapod class.

Characters of Aves. Feathers are modified epidermal scales which are found in all birds and only in birds. The fore limb is modified to form a wing (vestigial in a few forms). The heart is four-chambered. Birds are *endothermic,* that is, they maintain a high body temperature by producing heat through metabolic activity rather than by absorbing it from the environment.[3] All birds lay large-yolked, hard-shelled eggs which are incubated by the parents.

Subclasses of Aves. Although they are so numerous, birds show less diversity in basic anatomic structure than do the amphibians, reptiles, or mammals. Only two subclasses are recognized.

Subclass Archaeornithes. This subclass includes only a single genus of primitive birds from the Jurassic. In many ways *Ar-*

---

[3] The endothermic birds and mammals are often referred to as *homoiotherms.* "Homoiothermic" means having a constant body temperature.

chaeopteryx was intermediate between the reptiles and the birds. It had a long jaw armed with teeth, and digits with claws were present on the wings. The tail, though it was edged with feathers, was long and reptile-like with twenty vertebrae.

Archaeopteryx lithographica is an example of Archaeornithes.

Subclass Neornithes. All other birds have thirteen or fewer compressed tail vertebrae with the tail proper composed of a fan of feathers. The bones of the wing are reduced in number and, with few exceptions, clawed digits are absent. One extinct form (*Hesperornis*) had teeth, but all others have a horny bill instead. Modern birds are divided into about twenty-seven different orders. Among the most important of these are: Anseriformes, strong-flying, aquatic birds, including ducks, geese, and swans; Falconiformes, diurnal birds of prey, including hawks, eagles, and vultures; Galliformes, grain-eating birds, such as pheasants, turkeys, chickens, and quails; and Passeriformes, the perching birds, including the familiar small song birds, warblers, sparrows, thrushes, etc.

CLASS MAMMALIA

The active and intelligent mammals are considered the "highest" of the vertebrates. This is not just because we ourselves belong to this group, but because the development of the cerebral hemispheres of the brain, which has allowed man very largely to free himself from environmental restraints, is a characteristic trend of the class as a whole.

Characters of Mammalia. The feature from which the class draws its name is the presence of mammary glands which secrete milk for the nourishment of the young. All mammals, even the apparently naked whales, have some hair, and hair is found only in mammals. Like the birds, mammals are endothermic and have a four-chambered heart. Teeth set in sockets in the jaws are normally present. About 3,200 species of living mammals are known.

Subclasses of Mammalia. The mammals are divided into two subclasses, largely on the basis of reproductive habits.

Subclass Prototheria. This subclass includes only a single order, Monotremata, comprising three primitive species found only in the Australian region. In contrast to all other mammals, they lay eggs instead of bearing their young alive. After hatching, the young are nourished by the secretions of mammary glands which open directly to the surface of the skin in the abdominal region. The young suck the milk from tufts of hair growing in the region of these glands. (Fig. 2-6.)

Subclass Theria. All mammals other than the Prototheria bear their young alive. The secretions of the mammary glands reach the surface through nipples or teats which the young grasp in their mouths while nursing. There are two infraclasses of Theria with living members and several extinct infraclasses.

INFRACLASS METATHERIA. All living members of this infraclass belong to the order Marsupialia. The opossum and its allies inhabit South and Central America, with one species, the Virginia opossum, widespread in southern and eastern United States. All other marsupials are confined to the Australia region where they have undergone an extensive adaptive radiation. In addition to the familiar kangaroos, the group includes such forms as the Tasmanian wolf (*Thylacinus*), the

FIG. 2-6. Mammals: Top, a representative of the Prototheria, the duckbill platypus (*Ornithorhynchus*); bottom, a representative of the Metatheria, the Virginia opossum (*Didelphis virginiana*).

marsupial mole (*Notoryctes*), and the squirrel-like phalangers. There is no true allantoic placenta formation. The young are born in a very immature state and are carried for a time in a pouch on the belly of the female. (Fig. 2-6.)

INFRACLASS EUTHERIA. The most numerous and widespread of the mammals are the ones in which the young undergo a relatively long period of intra-uterine development, during which they receive nourishment from the maternal bloodstream through a placenta. The extant Eutheria are divided into about sixteen orders. Only eight of the more important ones will be considered here.

Order Insectivora. The moles, shrews, and hedgehogs have not departed greatly from the primitive eutherian pattern. They are small animals; indeed some of the shrews are the smallest of all mammals. Most have long, pointed snouts and jaws armed with sharp-pointed teeth.

Order Chiroptera. Bats are the only real flying mammals. As in the pterosaurs, the wing surface is formed of a membrane rather than of feathers, but in bats it is supported by the last four digits of the fore limb rather than just the fourth digit. Otherwise, the bats have not departed widely from the primitive insectivorous body plan. Most are insectivorous, some are fruit-eaters, and a few live by sucking blood from other animals.

Order Primates. The lemurs, monkeys, apes, and man are largely arboreal animals not greatly specialized except in the cerebral portion of the brain which is more highly developed than in any other animal. Even those forms that have returned to the ground show evidence of arboreal ancestry. The limbs are unusually long and the hands and feet are well developed and adapted for grasping.

Order Carnivora. The flesh-eating mammals form a diverse assemblage including such forms as cats, dogs, bears, and weasels. They have large, well developed canine teeth. The limbs are typically pentadactyl with digits having strong claws. The marine carnivores—seals, sea lions, and walruses—are sometimes placed in a separate order, Pinnipedia.

Order Perissodactyla. The "odd-toed" ungulates (horses, tapirs, and rhinoceroses) are herbivorous animals that walk on the tips of the toes. The primitive mammalian claws have been replaced by hooves. The long axis of the leg passes through the third digit, and the other toes are more or less reduced.

Order Artiodactyla. The cloven-hoofed or "even-toed" ungulates include such varied types as cattle, deer, pigs, antelopes, giraffes, and camels. Like the perissodactyls, they walk on the tips of the digits, but the long axis of the leg passes between the third and fourth digits, with the first, second, and fifth toes more or less reduced.

The white-tailed deer, *Odocoileus virginianus,* is an example of Artiodactyla.

Order Cetacea. Whales and dolphins are marine animals, streamlined in body form, the forelimbs modified to form paddles and the hind limbs lost. The tail is flattened and laterally expanded. The order includes the largest of all mammals, the blue whale, for which a length of 103 feet has been recorded.

The harbor porpoise, *Phocaena phocaena*, is an example of Cetacea.

Order Rodentia. Rodents, usually small animals, are by far the most numerous and widespread of all mammals. They possess two elongated, chisel-shaped incisors, one on each side of the upper and lower jaw. Some rodents are arboreal (squirrels), some terrestrial (rats and mice), some fossorial (pocket gophers), some aquatic (beavers).

MAJOR GROUPINGS OF VERTEBRATE CLASSES

Various authors have, from time to time, grouped the vertebrates into categories above the class but below the level of the subphylum. Since the names for these groups have become rather firmly entrenched in the literature, we include Figure 2-7 to show just which vertebrate classes are placed in these categories.

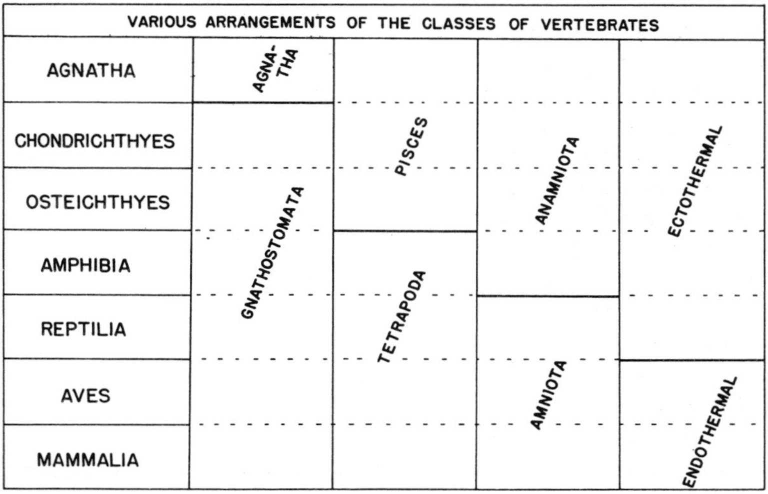

VARIOUS ARRANGEMENTS OF THE CLASSES OF VERTEBRATES				
AGNATHA	AGNATHA			
CHONDRICHTHYES	GNATHOSTOMATA	PISCES	ANAMNIOTA	ECTOTHERMAL
OSTEICHTHYES				
AMPHIBIA		TETRAPODA		
REPTILIA			AMNIOTA	
AVES				ENDOTHERMAL
MAMMALIA				

Fig. 2-7. Diagram showing various ways of grouping the classes of living vertebrates on the basis of jaws, limbs, embryonic membranes, and temperature regulation.

OUTLINE CLASSIFICATION OF LIVING VERTEBRATES

Class Agnatha
    Order Cyclostomata
Class Chondrichthyes
    Order Elasmobranchii
    Order Holocephali
Class Osteichthyes
   Subclass Actinopterygii
    Superorder Chondrostei
    Superorder Holostei
    Superorder Teleostei
      Orders Isospondyli, Ostariophysi, Percomorphi, etc.
   Subclass Choanichthyes
    Order Dipnoi
    Order Crossopterygii
Class Amphibia
   Superorder Lepospondyli
    Order Trachystomata
    Order Caudata
    Order Apoda
   Superorder Salientia
    Order Anura
Class Reptilia
   Subclass Anapsida
    Order Testudinata
   Subclass Lepidosauria
    Order Rhynchocephalia
    Order Squamata
   Subclass Archosauria
    Order Crocodilia
Class Aves
   Subclass Neornithes
    Orders Anseriformes, Falconiformes, Galliformes, Passeri-
      formes, etc.
Class Mammalia
   Subclass Prototheria
    Order Monotremata

Subclass Theria
  Infraclass Metatheria
    Order Marsupialia
  Infraclass Eutheria
    Orders Insectivora, Primates, Carnivora, Rodentia, etc.

3

Cells and Tissues

In the final analysis, the organs and organ systems that we study in comparative anatomy are composed of tissues which are made up of cells. Furthermore, the organ systems are engaged, for the most part, in supplying the cells and tissues with the items necessary for their vital processes and in keeping them in an appropriate environment. Hence, while comparative anatomy is basically a comparative study of organ systems, an understanding of cells and tissues is necessary for a full appreciation of the entire complex structure of the vertebrate body.

THE CELL.

While there is no such thing as a "typical" cell, cells are enough alike so that we can get an understanding of them by considering a diagrammatic cell.

Gross Cell Structure. The outer portion of the living cell is made up of the *cell* (or *plasma*) *membrane.* It is not just a simple boundary but a functional membrane that controls the entrances and exits of various materials concerned with the metabolism of the cell.

Within a generalized animal cell, we can distinguish two parts: *cytoplasm* and *nucleus*. The cytoplasm contains a number of highly organized components. The *endoplasmic reticulum* is found throughout most of the cytoplasm. It seems to be an elaborately organized network of tubule-like structures which play an active part in the synthesis of compounds by the cell. *Mitochondria*, small bodies associated with oxidative reactions, are scattered throughout the cytoplasm. In a living cell they are in ceaseless motion. Although outside the nuclear membrane, the *centrosome* and the one or two *centrioles* contained therein seem to function as part of the nucleus. They are concerned with cell division.

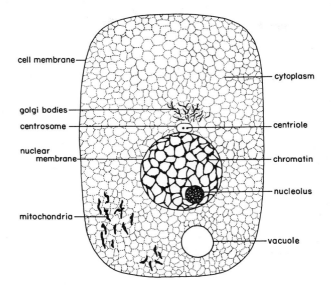

FIG. 3-1. Diagrammatic sketch of a typical animal cell.

Inside the cell, oftentimes but not invariably near the middle, is the nucleus. It is surrounded by a *nuclear membrane* somewhat similar to the cell membrane mentioned above and contains a protoplasm known as *nucleoplasm*. Within the nucleoplasm can be seen *chromatin material* which is the stuff of which *chromosomes* are made. Inside of the nucleus are one or more tiny *nucleoli*.

In addition to the parts mentioned above, cells may contain other inclusions. For example, droplets of fat are sometimes present in the cytoplasm. Fibrils are characteristic of muscle and nerve cells but they may be present in other types of cells.

Shape and Size of Cells. Cells vary enormously in shape. Some, such as egg cells, are round. Some epithelial cells are very flat, others are cuboidal in shape. Smooth muscle cells are generally spindle-shaped. Nerve cells have many processes, some of which, in the larger animals, may be several feet long. Cells also vary in size. Some are about .01 mm. in diameter, but others are much smaller and the yolk of an ostrich egg, which is a single cell, is several inches in diameter.

Chemical Constituents. Water is the most abundant constituent of protoplasm. In solution in the protoplasm are a number of inorganic salts, but the most important elements of protoplasm are formed from the four basic organic compounds: carbohydrates, fats, proteins, and nucleic acids.

Metabolism is the sum total of the chemical processes by which protoplasm is produced and maintained. Much of a vertebrate's structure and functioning is concerned, directly or indirectly, with the collection, transformation, and transportation to the cells of the materials that are needed for their proper maintenance and function, and the removal and elimination of such wastes as are formed by the metabolic activity of the cells.

TISSUES

In all vertebrates, cells which are similar in structure and function are grouped together as tissues. While many different functions are assigned to cells and tissues in the body, we can group the tissues into four major categories: epithelial, sustentative, contractile, and nervous (Fig. 3-2).

Epithelial Tissue. Epithelial tissue, or epithelium, can be defined as the tissue that covers both external and internal body surfaces and lines cavities, vessels, and ducts. Epithelial tissues play significant roles in metabolism and may be concerned with such functions as secretion, excretion, respiration, and absorption. Epithelial cells may be flattened (*squamous*), square (*cuboidal*) or elongated (*columnar*). Columnar epithelial cells sometimes bear cilia on their free edges. Basically, two types of epithelial tissue are recognized: simple epithelium which is composed of a single layer of cells; and stratified epithelium which is made up of several layers of cells.

Sustentative Tissue. Sustentative tissues are distinguished by the presence of an intercellular material, or *matrix*. The different sorts of sustentative tissue are defined, in part, by the nature of this matrix. Sometimes these tissues are all called connective tissues but it seems better to restrict this term to the so-called connective tissues proper which do have the function of binding other tissues together.

Connective Tissue. Connective tissue is a sustentative tissue in which the intercellular matrix is composed primarily of fibers

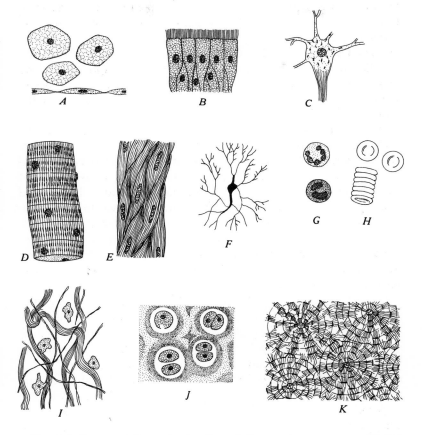

F$_{IG}$. 3-2. Representative animal cells and tissues. *A*, squamous epithelial cells; *B*, ciliated columnar epithelium; *C*, the cell body of a neuron; *D*, striated muscle; *E*, smooth muscle; *F*, a neuron; *G*, white blood cells; *H*, red blood cells; *I*, connective tissue; *J*, cartilage; *K*, bone.

imbedded in an amorphous ground substance. Some connective tissues are loosely organized, with the fibers scattered and the connective tissue cells more numerous. Such tissues are found in the walls of blood vessels, between the skin and underlying muscles, etc. Other connective tissues have fewer cells and the fibers are numerous and densely matted. This densely organized connective tissue is found in the skin and in the walls of the digestive tract. Sometimes the fibers are organized to run parallel to each other, as in the *tendons* by which muscles are fastened to bones, and in the *ligaments* which join bones and support internal organs.

Fluid Tissue. In fluid tissue, the *blood* and *lymph*, the matrix is a liquid, the *plasma*, in which the cells are suspended. Blood contains both red blood cells (*erythrocytes*) and various types of white blood cells (*leukocytes*). Erythrocytes are lacking in the lymph.

Supporting Tissue. These are the tissues that comprise the skeleton and other hard parts of the vertebrate body. *Cartilage* is a sustentative tissue in which the abundant matrix is solidified to form a firm, rather flexible, supporting tissue. *Bone*, the chief supporting tissue of the majority of the vertebrates, has a hard and rigid consistency resulting from the extensive deposit of inorganic salts within the matrix.

Contractile Tissue. Contractile tissues are those that contract; in the vertebrate body these are known as *muscles*. We recognize three major types of muscles.

Smooth or Involuntary. These muscles are composed of spindle-shaped cells which are frequently arranged in sheets or bundles. They make up the contractile tissue associated with the digestive system, blood vessels, and certain ducts in the body. Their action is rather slow and is not under control of the will.

Striated or Voluntary. These muscles are bundles of long, striated, multinucleate fibers which are usually associated with the skeleton and hence are commonly known as *skeletal muscles*. They comprise the great bulk of the body musculature. They contract rapidly and are under voluntary control.

Cardiac. This is the muscle of which the heart is formed. It is composed of branching, interconnected fibers which are striated as are the skeletal muscle fibers mentioned above. However, like smooth muscle, it is not under control of the will.

Nervous Tissue. One of the features of protoplasm is responsiveness to stimuli. All protoplasm is responsive to a degree but

certain types of cells called *neurons* have the properties of con-
ductivity and responsiveness more highly developed than do any
other cells of the body. A neuron has a cell body containing the
nucleus, and two or more processes: the *axon* is the process that
carries impulses away from the cell body; the *dendrites* are
processes that carry impulses to the cell body. Groups of these
neurons, together with various supporting and protecting cells
(*neuroglia* and *sheath cells*), are organized into nervous tissue.

4

Vertebrate Development

The adult animal is simply the last in a series of developmental stages through which the organism passes during its lifetime. Therefore, a quick review of the embryonic stages of the developing vertebrate will give a basis for an understanding of the major organ systems and how they have differentiated, together with an understanding of the basic vertebrate body plan. To save space, we shall not try here to trace in any detail the developmental stages of a series of different embryos. Although amphioxus is not a vertebrate, its embryonic development shows in simple, almost diagrammatic, fashion the major stages of vertebrate development. The following discussion is based more nearly on amphioxus than on any other individual animal.

EGGS

Since vertebrates always reproduce sexually, development begins with a single cell, the *zygote,* or fertilized egg.

Egg Types. There are three major types of vertebrate eggs, classified primarily on the basis of the amount of yolk contained therein.

Oligolecithal or Meiolecithal. These are eggs in which there is a small amount of yolk. They are found in amphioxus and most mammals. (Mammal eggs are sometimes spoken of as *alecithal,* i.e., without yolk, but they probably always have some yolk granules.)

Mesolecithal. Mesolecithal eggs have a moderate amount of yolk. Primitive fishes, lungfishes, and amphibians have eggs of this type.

Polylecithal. Eggs that have a large amount of yolk are classed as polylecithal. Such eggs are found in the elasmobranchs, the higher fishes, reptiles, birds, and the egg-laying mammals.

Eggs are sometimes classified according to the distribution of the yolk. If the yolk is rather evenly distributed throughout the cytoplasm, as it is in an oligolecithal egg, the egg is spoken of as *isolecithal* or *homolecithal*. Since the yolk is heavier than the cytoplasm, in mesolecithal and polylecithal eggs it tends to settle in the lower hemisphere of the egg. These eggs are known as *telolecithal*.

Polarity. The presence of a moderate or large amount of yolk which tends to settle brings the first evidence of orientation in the vertebrate egg. The upper pole, which contains the nucleus and some cytoplasm but in which little yolk is present, is known as the *animal pole*. The lower pole, in which the yolk is concentrated, is the *vegetal pole*. After radial symmetry has been established by the development of polarity in the vertebrate egg, bilateral symmetry is established by a plane which divides the egg into right and left halves. The axis of this plane is sometimes determined simply by the point of entrance of the sperm, but in some forms, the plane of symmetry appears to be determined before the sperm ever enters the egg.

CLEAVAGE TYPES

Once the egg has been fertilized, development proceeds by mitotic divisions of the zygote, with the subsequent formation of daughter cells (*blastomeres*). These divisions are known as cleavages. In the vertebrates, two types of cleavage are known.

Holoblastic Cleavage. In holoblastic cleavage, the cleavage planes pass entirely through the egg. Holoblastic cleavage is characteristic of oligolecithal and mesolecithal eggs. These cleavages may result in daughter cells that are about equal in size (in oligolecithal eggs) or they may be so placed that the daughter cells are quite unequal in size (in mesolecithal eggs). Thus the type of division shown by amphioxus eggs is holoblastic and the daughter cells are nearly equal; on the other hand, cleavage in frog eggs is also holoblastic but the cleavage planes are concentrated near the animal pole so that the upper cells (*micromeres*) are smaller than the cells in the region of the vegetal pole (*macromeres*).

Meroblastic Cleavage. In meroblastic cleavage, which is characteristic of polylecithal eggs, the cleavage planes pass through the cytoplasm but do not continue on through the yolk; hence, the cleavage planes pass only part of the way through the entire egg. This type of cleavage is exemplified by the developing chicken egg.

BLASTULA FORMATION

As the original fertilized egg divides and redivides into daughter cells by the devlopment of cleavage planes, the daughter cells become smaller and smaller. They come to form more or less a sphere consisting of a layer of cells surrounding a central cavity. The embryo at this stage is known as a *blastula* and the cavity is known as the *blastocoel* or *segmentation cavity*. The wall of the blastula of amphioxus is never more than a single layer of cells thick; however, in other animals such as the frog, several layers of cells may surround the blastocoel.

GASTRULATION

When development has proceeded to the stage where a well developed blastula has formed, the cells in the region of what will ultimately be the postero-dorsal portion of the embryo begin to invaginate or fold inward. As the infolding layer becomes larger, it tends to reduce the size of the original cavity or blastocoel. At the same time, however, the invagination produces a sort of inner sac, the *primitive gut* or *archenteron*, with the formation of a new cavity, the *gastrocoel* or *cavity of the archenteron*. This cavity leads to the outside by means of an opening now known as the *blastopore*. The inward-folding layer of cells ultimately comes in contact with the inner wall of the original blastula, thus obliterating the blastocoel. At this stage, then, we have a two-layered structure known as a *gastrula*, containing the cavity of the archenteron which opens to the outside by means of the blastopore. The inner of the two layers may be appropriately referred to as the *hypoblast* and the outer as the *epiblast*. In many texts these two layers are known respectively as endoderm and ectoderm; we shall reserve these terms for use in a later, more appropriate stage of development.

GERM LAYER FORMATION AND DIFFERENTIATION

The primary cell layers of the developing embryo—*endoderm, mesoderm,* and *ectoderm*—are known as germ layers. The processes of germ layer formation and differentiation described below are perhaps most similar to those of amphioxus, but are intended only to point out the basic developmental pattern and do not pretend to be the descriptive embryology of any particular animal.

Differentiation of Hypoblast. The hypoblast gives rise not only to the true endoderm but also to the mesoderm and notochord.

Mesoderm Formation. In amphioxus, pouches of hypoblast material along the dorsal wall of the archenteron, to the right and left of the mid-dorsal line, push outward or evaginate to give rise to tissue now known as mesoderm. The cavities formed as these pouches develop remain as permanent cavities and are the first evidence of the coelom. In most vertebrates, however, the mesoderm masses form as solid sheets and later develop splits which are the beginning of the coelom.

Notochord. On the dorsal wall of the hypoblast, a mass of cells pinches off along the midline to become the notochord. This lies dorsal to the hypoblast and between the two mesodermal masses.

Endoderm. Once the notochord and mesodermal pouches have been formed, what is left of the hypoblast may now appropriately be called *endoderm*. Most modern workers feel that it is inappropriate to term this layer endoderm until after the mesoderm and notochord have been formed; they use the term "hypoblast" to describe this group of cells in the stage preceding mesoderm and notochord formation.

Differentiation of Epiblast. While the hypoblast has been giving rise to the mesoderm, notochord, and endoderm, the epiblast has also been differentiating. The epiblast in the mid-dorsal region forms a thickened plate of cells (*neural,* or *medullary, plate*) which forms the *neurectoderm.* The epiblast on the rest of the developing embryo forms the *skin ectoderm.* The neural plate folds up along each side to produce a groove. The embryo is then said to be in the *neural groove stage.* The walls of the groove,

known as the *neural folds*, grow upward and inward and ultimately meet to form a true tube; the embryo is now in the *neural
tube stage*. The tube is then covered over and sinks below the
surface as the skin ectoderm from the two sides fuses above it.
Dorsolateral masses of cells are pinched off on either side of the
tube to form the *neural crests*. It is the neural tube that gives rise
to the hollow, dorsal nerve cord (neural cord) and brain.

Differentiation of Mesoderm. The mesodermal masses formed
on either side of the notochord (between the ectoderm and endoderm) now differentiate further. The mesoderm lateral to the
notochord and well above the coelom becomes the *epimere*. The
mesoderm forming the dorsal wall of the coelom on each side
becomes the *mesomere*. The mesoderm which forms the inner and
outer walls of the coelom is known as *hypomere*. The hypomere
on the outer wall of the coelom is called *somatic* hypomere and
that on the inner wall, *splanchnic* hypomere.

DERIVATIVES OF THE GERM LAYERS

Embryonic development does not cease with the formation of
the three primary germ layers and their subdivisions described
above, but continues as a gradual, step-by-step development until
the entire adult animal is formed. The actual differentiation of
organs from the germ layers indeed begins before all of the germ
layers are completely formed. It would involve a tremendous
mass of detail to describe at this point the development of the
various organs and organ systems. However, we can conveniently
classify the organs according to their embryonic derivation and
trace their homologies by simply listing the structures derived
from each of the primary germ layers.

Ectoderm. The primary germ layer, the ectoderm, comprises
the epiblast and all the structures derived from it.

Epidermis. The entire outer covering of the body is formed
from ectoderm. This superficial layer includes the epidermis of
the skin and all of the structures that develop from it: skin glands,
epidermal scales, hairs, feathers, nails, claws, horns, etc.

Stomodaeum and Proctodaeum. At the anterior end of the
embryo an ectodermal invagination occurs, forming the *stomodaeum* or primitive mouth. Derivatives of the ectoderm which

lines the stomodaeum include the lining of the lips and mouth, the enamel of the teeth, glands in the oral cavity, the covering of the tongue, and the anterior and middle lobes of the pituitary gland.

At the posterior end of the body, a similar invagination known as the *proctodaeum* pushes inward to meet the posterior end of the archenteron. The proctodaeal ectoderm gives rise to the lining of the anal canal and, in the forms which have a cloaca, to a portion of the cloacal lining.

At first, the cavity of the stomodaeum is separated from the cavity of the archenteron by the *oral membrane* and the cavity of the proctodaeum is separated from it by the *anal membrane*. As soon as the oral and anal membranes rupture, we no longer speak of the archenteron but of the *enteron* or *true gut*, which is now a true tube, the *digestive tract*, extending from one end of the body to the other.

Nervous System. Since the neural tube was formed from the neurectoderm originally and since the entire central nervous system develops from the neural tube, it follows that the central nervous system is ectodermal in origin.

The entire peripheral nervous system is also formed from ectodermal cells, either from cells of the neural crests, from the neural tube itself, or from *placodes* formed of superficial ectoderm.

Pituitary Body. A ventral evagination of the floor of the brain forms the *infundibulum,* which grows down to meet an evagination from the roof of the stomodaeum known as *Rathke's pouch* (*hypophyseal pouch*). The two grow together to form the pituitary body.

Sense Organs. The sensory parts of the sense organs are also derived from ectoderm. The *optic cup* which gives rise to the retina is itself simply an outgrowth from the wall of the central nervous system. This cup comes to surround the lens of the eye which develops from the outer, or superficial, ectoderm.

The organs of smell are first recognizable as *olfactory placodes* which develop on either side of the head. These thickened placodes finally invaginate into *olfactory pits* which may secondarily become connected with the stomodaeum.

Auditory placodes which are destined to form the inner ear also develop from ectodermal cells on either side of the posterior part of the head. In the lower vertebrates, a *lateral line system* is developed from placodes along the side of the head and the body.

Endoderm. The endoderm is the inner layer of cells which originally lined the cavity of the archenteron. It is what remains of the hypoblast after the notochord and mesoderm have differentiated.

Lining of Gut. As we have noted (p. 37), the oral and anal membranes rupture, making the archenteron continuous with the stomodaeum and proctodaeum and thus forming the enteron or true gut. The lining of the gut, therefore, is endodermal.

Structures Derived from Enteron. Structures formed as evaginations of the enteron are likewise at least partially endodermal in origin. Thus, two important digestive glands, the *liver* and *pancreas*, which arise as diverticula from the digestive tract, are lined with endoderm. The lungs are also diverticula from the original digestive tract and are lined with endodermal epithelium.

In the pharyngeal region of the digestive tract, several pairs of pouches push outward from the wall of the pharynx through the mesoderm until they come in contact with the ectoderm covering the body. At this point, the endoderm of the pharynx fuses with the ectoderm of the outer body covering. When these pouches break through to the outside, the openings are known as the *visceral slits*. If these visceral slits, or clefts, have gills associated with them, they are then appropriately called *gill slits*. The septa separating the pouches are the *visceral arches*. In the higher vertebrates (the amniotes) the pouches form but rarely perforate. The first pouch develops into the Eustachian tube and the middle ear. The others give rise to groups of cells which form various structures such as the palatine tonsils, the thymus gland, the parathyroid glands, and the small, irregular masses known as ultimobranchial bodies. Hence, these structures are all endodermal in origin.

Excretory Structures. The urinary bladder is derived from the endoderm of the posterior portion of the gut, as is the *urethra*, the tube which, in the mammals, carries urine from the bladder to the outside.

Mesoderm. Much of the mesoderm forms structures directly in place, but part of it remains as an undifferentiated, loosely organized tissue known as *mesenchyme*, which has the ability to migrate to other regions of the body and to differentiate there. Mesenchyme gives rise to the circulatory system and to muscle, bone, and connective tissue. The primary divisions of the mesoderm, as mentioned above (p. 36), are epimere, mesomere, and hypomere (Fig. 4-1).

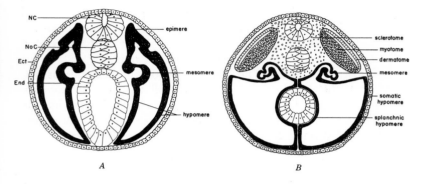

Fig. 4-1. Diagram showing fate of the mesoderm. A, prior to division of epimere; B, after division of epimere. NC, neural cord; NoC, notochord; Ect, ectoderm; End, endoderm.

Epimere. On each side of the body, the epimere segments into a longitudinal row of blocks, the mesodermal somites, each of which further differentiates into three parts.

SCLEROTOME. The medial portion of the epimere, next to the notochord and neutral tube, is known as sclerotome. It gives rise to vertebral structures which surround the notochord and the nerve cord, and to mesenchyme which forms bony and cartilaginous structures elsewhere.

DERMATOME. The lateral portion of the epimere, that which is in contact with the skin ectoderm, is known as dermatome. It forms the *dermis,* the inner layer of the skin.

MYOTOME. The portion of the epimere between the median sclerotome and the lateral dermatome is the myotome. The myotomal segments, which are separated from one another by septa called *myocommata* or *myosepta,* give rise to the large skeletal muscle masses that make up such a large part of the vertebrate body.

Mesomere. The mesomere develops into the urogenital organs (kidney structures and gonads) and their ducts. The terminal portions of the ducts are sometimes lined with ectodermal, or occasionally endodermal, epithelium.

Hypomere. The hypomere (p. 36) is divided into an inner, *splanchnic* hypomere and an outer, *somatic* hypomere.

SPLANCHNIC HYPOMERE. The splanchnic hypomere fuses with the endoderm that constitutes the wall of the gut to form the *splanchnopleure*. Splanchnic hypomere is largely mesenchymal in nature and gives rise to such structures as the connective tissue and smooth muscle of the gut, the heart and its related blood vessels, and various mesenteries and ligaments.

SOMATIC HYPOMERE. The somatic hypomere becomes associated with the ectoderm of the body wall to form the *somatopleure*. Somatic hypomere gives rise to such tissue as the *pericardium* which surrounds the heart, the *pleura* which covers the lungs and lines the pleural cavity, and the *peritoneum*.

EMBRYONIC MEMBRANES

Many vertebrate embryos develop one or more *embryonic membranes* (sometimes called *extraembryonic membranes*) which lie outside the body of the embryo and are lost at birth. These are: the *yolk sac*, found in some anamniotes and all amniotes; and the *amnion, chorion,* and *allantois,* present in all amniotes and only in them. (See Fig. 4-2.)

Yolk Sac. In forms that have meroblastic cleavage, a fold of tissue grows down to surround the mass of yolk. Among the lower vertebrates, such as the sharks, all three of the primary germ layers are included in the yolk sac. The endoderm surrounds the yolk and the mesoderm gives rise to the vitelline blood vessels by which the nutrients of the yolk are conveyed to the embryo. The yolk sac of the reptiles, birds, and egg-laying mammals is composed only of endoderm and mesoderm. Even the higher mammals, though they have almost no yolk, develop a small yolk sac similar to that of the reptiles from which they evolved.

Amnion and Chorion. Folds of ectoderm and mesoderm grow up around the developing amniote embryo. They meet and fuse above it to form two sacs: the inner one (amnion) encloses the embryo in a fluid-filled cavity; the outer one (chorion) surrounds the whole complex of embryo and other embryonic membranes.

Allantois. A fourth embryonic membrane, the allantois, grows out from the posterior end of the amniote gut to form a large sac lying against the chorion. It is composed of endoderm and mesoderm. The allantois serves as a storage place for excretory wastes and, in conjunction with the chorion, as a respiratory membrane.

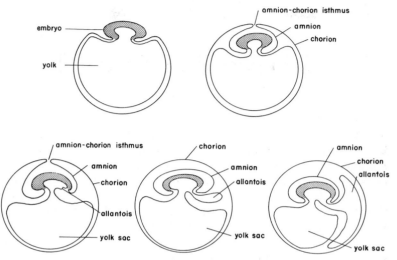

FIG. 4-2. Diagram showing the formation of the embryonic membranes in the developing amniote. (From *Introduction to Herpetology* by Coleman J. Goin and Olive B. Goin. San Francisco: W. H. Freeman and Company, copyright 1962.)

Placenta. Some animals are viviparous, that is, the young undergo embryonic development within the body of the mother and receive some or all of their nourishment from the maternal bloodstream, usually through a *placenta*. This is a dual organ, usually formed in part from the lining of the uterus and in part from one or more of the embryonic membranes. Viviparous sharks have a yolk sac placenta. Development takes place within the ovary of the live-bearing bony fishes and the placenta, when present, involves yolk sac and ovarian tissue.

The embryonic part of the amniote placenta is always formed partly from the chorion since it is the chorion that surrounds all the other embryonic membranes. A few lizards and snakes have a placenta formed of chorion and yolk sac, and a similar placenta is present transitorily in many marsupials. The fetal placenta of the eutherian mammals is formed largely from the allantois.

5

Integumentary System

The evolution (and hence the comparative anatomy) of the integumentary system is closely correlated with the evolution of the terrestrial vertebrates from the aquatic forms. Initially, the integument of the primitive, water-dwelling vertebrates was heavily armored for protection. With the development of life on land, this heavy, cumbersome armor tended to disappear and the integument became a smooth, fleshy, soft skin. As the vertebrates became more fully terrestrial, however, water conservation became a particularly important problem; this resulted in a secondary modification of the integumentary system—the development of an outer, water-impervious layer.

FUNCTIONS OF INTEGUMENTARY SYSTEM

The integumentary system—the skin together with its various derivatives—forms a wrapping around the outside of the body and comprises a multifunction system. Its principal functions are summarized below.

Protection. Since the integument completely encloses the body, it is inevitably the system that largely protects the internal structures from the outside world. In addition to shielding the body from simple mechanical injury, the skin also protects it from invasion by foreign organisms and foreign substances.

Color also plays an important role in protection. Coloration may be *cryptic,* so that the animal blends into its background and is concealed from potential predators. If an animal is dangerous or noxious, though, it may be brightly colored as a warning to its potential predators. The color of birds and mammals is largely determined by the color of the feathers or of the hair. In fishes, amphibians, and reptiles, coloration depends on the presence of pigment cells, *chromatophores,* in the integument. Some of these animals are able to change their color to blend in with changing backgrounds, partly by changes in the distribution of the pigment granules within the chromatophores and partly through changes in the position of the chromatophores within the skin.

Sensory Reception. Various sensory receptors (heat, cold, touch, etc.) by which the organism is informed of both inimical and beneficent forces in the outer world are located in the integument, which thus helps keep the organism aware of its external environment.

Excretion. Excretory functions are performed by several vertebrate integumentary systems. Among the fishes, some salt excretion takes place through the integument of the gills, and among the mammals elimination of salts is in part accomplished by the sweat glands of the skin.

Respiration. Respiratory functions of the skin are important for a number of vertebrates, particularly the amphibians. They have a thin skin which is kept moist by the secretion of numerous mucous glands. Large blood vessels bring a copious supply of blood close to the surface of the body. Exchange of gases (oxygen and carbon dioxide) takes place between the blood and air through the moist skin. One group of salamanders has become lungless and depends almost entirely upon the skin as a respiratory organ.

Temperature Control. Among the birds and mammals the skin and its derivatives (hair and feathers) serve a very important function in insulating the body against extremes of external temperature. The integument also acts partly as a thermostat, controlling the amount of heat that leaves the body by way of the skin. When the skin is cold, the small blood vessels in it contract, forcing the blood away from the surface of the body and thus reducing the amount of heat lost from the blood to the environment. When the skin is warm, the blood vessels expand so that more blood is brought close to the surface and more heat dissipated.

Evaporation of water secreted by the sweat glands is an important cooling mechanism in many mammals. Change of color in the lower vertebrates also plays a role in temperature control. When skin color is light, heat waves are reflected from the body of the animal; when the color of the skin is dark, heat waves are absorbed.

Water Regulation. Regulation of the water content of the body is, in part, accomplished by the skin. In marine and terrestrial vertebrates which live in a hyperosmotic environment, the skin prevents the too rapid loss of body water to the surrounding medium, while in fresh water forms, which live in a hypo-osmotic environment, it prevents the absorption of too much water.

Food Storage. Food storage is a significant function among the birds and mammals, since the fat in the deep layer of their skin acts as a reserve food supply.

Nourishment. The mammary glands of the mammals are derivatives of the skin and hence are a part of the integumentary system. Newborn mammals depend upon the milk secreted by these glands for nourishment.

Locomotion. The use of the integument as a locomotive apparatus is widespread throughout the classes of vertebrates. The webbing on the feet of ducks and frogs, the fins of fishes, the wing feathers of birds, the flight membranes of bats, and the belly scales of snakes are among the locomotory structures derived from the integument.

Miscellaneous Functions. In addition to the functions mentioned above, a number of others can be assigned to the integument of certain groups. For example, in some of the mammals the skin is the site of the manufacture of vitamin D. Some of the mammals and amphibians have skin pouches which serve as brood pouches for the developing young. Among the birds, differences in color and structure of the feathers facilitate sex recognition.

INTEGUMENT PROPER

While there is much diversity among the various groups of vertebrates in the structures derived from it, the integument itself is rather uniform in basic structure.

Structure of Integument. The vertebrate integument differs fundamentally from that of the invertebrates. Among the invertebrates, the integument generally consists of two distinct layers—an outer *cuticle* of noncellular material and an inner layer of a single tier of columnar cells forming the *hypodermis*.

Among the vertebrates, on the other hand, while the integument is also of two layers, these differ from those of the invertebrates.

Epidermis. The outer layer, or epidermis, is composed of stratified epithelium. The cells of the basal layer (*stratum germinativum*) of this epithelium continually go through mitotic divisions, forming new cells which are pushed toward the outside. As these cells approach the outer surface, they tend to become flattened and, in many cases, they produce a substance called *keratin,* which renders them tough and impervious to water. In the tetrapods, these cells lose their nuclei and die, so that the outer surface of the epidermis is formed of a tough, impervious layer of dead cells, the *stratum corneum.* When a stratum corneum is formed, it may be shed in tiny flakes and patches, or it may be shed as an entire sheet at one time. This process is called *ecdysis* or *molting*. As a result of the shedding or wearing away of the outer layer of the epidermis as new cells are formed by the basal layer, the epidermis tends to remain relatively constant in thickness.

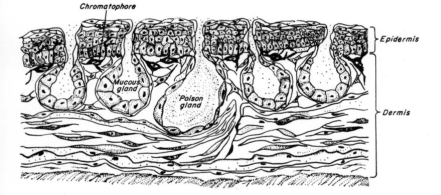

FIG. 5-1. Cross section through the skin of a frog. (From *Introduction to Herpetology* by Coleman J. Goin and Olive B. Goin. San Francisco: W. H. Freeman and Company, copyright 1962.)

Dermis. The deep layer of the integument of the vertebrates comprises the dermis. It is generally much thicker than the epidermis and is composed of connective tissue, blood vessels, lymphatic vessels, fat, and such additional structures as nerves, the bases of glands, and pigment cells. (See Fig. 5-1.)

Comparative Anatomy of Integument Proper. The skin of the vertebrates has many derivatives; some of them are unique to one group or another, while others are more widespread. Two of the most widely distributed are *glands* and *scales*. These integumentary derivatives will be discussed separately from the skin proper.

Agnatha. In the cyclostomes, the skin is thin and soft. The outer epidermis is quite glandular; the glands are all single cell structures. Since in Agnatha there is no degeneration of the epithelial cells as they approach the surface, no stratum corneum is formed. The dermis of the cyclostomes is a thin layer, actually thinner than the epidermis. No scales of any sort are present over the body integument; the few horny structures in the buccal funnel and on the tongue are the only epidermal cornifications in this group.

Chondrichthyes and Osteichthyes. Among both the cartilaginous and bony fishes the integument shows two significant changes over the condition found in the cyclostomes. Dermal scales are present and the skin contains multicellular as well as unicellular glands. The integument, like that of the cyclostomes, lacks any dead corneal layer; hence, no stratum corneum is ever formed. In a few of the teleosts, however, certain little "pearl organs" appear as cornified papillae in the epidermis during the breeding season.

Amphibia. Two important changes are found in the skin of the amphibians as compared with that of the fishes. First, the dermal scales have largely disappeared; the only scales present in living amphibians are some tiny ones buried in the skin of some of the caecilians, and larger bony plates on the back of a few of the toads. The second difference in the amphibian skin is that the epidermis, for the first time in the evolutionary sequence, develops a layer of dead epithelial cells at the surface and thus has a true stratum corneum. In general, among the amphibians there is a correlation between the degree of terrestrialism and the formation of the stratum corneum, which is best developed in those that spend the most time on land.

The dermis, since it is a significant organ of respiration among the amphibians, is unusually well supplied with blood vessels.

Reptilia. The epidermis of the reptiles has an extremely well developed corneal layer. Also, we find in the reptiles for the first time well developed epidermal scales. Indeed, this is the major feature in the evolution of their integument. While it is true that some dermal scales persist in a few of the reptiles, all of them have epidermal scales. Stratum corneum and scales form a waterproof outer covering which, by reducing water loss, admirably adapts the reptiles to life on land. Associated with this adaptation is a reduction in the number of skin glands; a few of the reptiles lack integumentary glands. The reptilian dermis is thicker than that of the amphibian. Skins of some of the reptiles can be prepared into leather having a high commercial value.

Aves. The skin of birds is rather thin compared with that of the reptiles. While a few birds (such as the ostrich) have skins thick enough to be prepared as leather, in most of them the dermis is very thin. The epidermis has lost much of the thick, corneal, outer layer of the reptiles except in exposed places such as the legs and feet. Otherwise, the integument is covered with unique avian structures, the *feathers*, which are modifications of the stratum corneum.

Mammalia. The dermis of mammals is usually quite thick and tough and forms a good leather. Except in a few mammals, the epidermal scales have largely disappeared. A new corneal derivative, the unique *hair*, has been developed.

GLANDS

Epithelial cells specialized to perform a secretory function are known as *gland cells*. They may be scattered singly through an epithelial tissue, *unicellular glands*, or numbers of them may be gathered together to form discrete organs, the *multicellular glands*. The epidermis of the vertebrate integument is composed of epithelial tissue, and is frequently rich in glands.

Types of Glands. The glands of the vertebrate body may be divided into two distinct groups: *endocrine* and *exocrine*.

Endocrine Glands. The endocrine glands possess no ducts; the glandular secretions seep through the membranes of the gland cells to enter the blood stream which transports them to other parts of the body. Some endocrine glands arise from the embryonic ectodermal epithelium, but they are not really associated with the integument. They are very important in the co-ordination of bodily functions and will be discussed further in Chapter 15.

Exocrine Glands. Exocrine glands empty their products directly onto an epithelial surface or into a duct which transports the secretion from the cavity of the gland to some region away from the gland. A number of exocrine glands are not associated with the skin (e.g., certain digestive glands) and these will be discussed under other systems. On the other hand, many exocrine glands are present in the vertebrate integument and are properly discussed in relation to it.

In general, exocrine integumentary glands can be divided into three types: *holocrine, merocrine,* and *apocrine.*

HOLOCRINE GLANDS. In these glands the individual cells producing the secretion rupture and die when the secretion is released; further secretion depends upon the formation of new cells. Sebaceous (oil) glands are of this type.

MEROCRINE GLANDS. In these glands, the cell releases the secretion without injury to the cell itself. Sweat glands are examples of this type of gland.

APOCRINE GLANDS. There is destruction of part of the cytoplasm of the secreting cells of apocrine glands, but the actual cells themselves are not destroyed. The mammary glands are representative apocrine glands.

Comparative Anatomy of Integumentary Glands. The glands of the integument form in the epidermis, though they may grow down into the dermis.

Agnatha. Unicellular merocrine glands are the only integumentary glands found among the cyclostomes. The prolific production of mucus by the skin glands of the hagfish covers the body with an enormous amount of slimy material.

Chondrichthyes and Osteichthyes. The cartilaginous and bony fishes have, in addition to numerous unicellular glands, well developed sets of multicellular mucous glands. A few of the elasmobranchs and bony fishes have multicellular glands modified into poison glands for protection. These glands are associated with spines on the fins or operculum, by which the poison may be injected. Special glandular structures found in the fishes are the *luminescent organs* in the skin of some fishes living in the deep sea, and the *pterygopodial glands* found at the base of the clasping organs of certain elasmobranchs.

Amphibia. The amphibian skin is extremely glandular. Except for the unicellular *glands of Leydig,* which occur in the epidermis of certain larval salamanders, the skin glands of the amphibians are multicellular and are of two sorts. _Mucous glands_ are extremely numerous in the skin of most amphibians. Since the amphibian skin is a respiratory organ and since respiratory surfaces must be kept moist, these mucous glands have an extremely important function in keeping the outer surface of the skin moist.

In addition to mucous glands, a number of amphibians have poison glands in the skin. The _parotoid_ glands in the shoulder region of the common toad, for example, are actually masses of poison glands. Certain tropical frogs produce extremely poisonous secretions which were used by Indians for poisoning the tips of their arrows.

Reptilia. Correlated with the marked development of the stratum corneum and the formation of epidermal scales which completely cover the body of the reptile, there has been a significant reduction in the number of integumentary glands. Crocodilians and certain turtles have _musk glands_ along the lower side of the lower jaw and turtles may have them along the side of the body between the plastron and the carapace. In the crocodilians, glands are present along the back between the rows of dermal plates. Crocodilians and snakes have glands associated with the cloaca which produce a musky-smelling secretion. Some of the lizards are apparently entirely devoid of skin glands.

Aves. Like their reptilian ancestors, birds have a reduced number of skin glands. The most common integumentary gland among the birds is the _uropygial gland_ at the base of the tail, which secretes oils used in preening the feathers. A few birds also have modified oil glands associated with the external ear opening.

Mammalia. The mammalian integument is extremely rich in glands. It has been estimated, for example, that on the average there are about two and one-half million _sweat_, or _sudoriparous_, _glands_ on the human body, although occasionally an abnormality occurs in which sweat glands are absent. The _mammary glands_, which give this class its name, are thought to be modified sweat glands. They produce milk for the nourishment of the young—a unique feature found only in mammals. _Sebaceous_, or _oil_, _glands_ are very common in the skins of mammals. In addition, there are glands associated with the eyelids (the _Meibomian glands_ and the _glands of Zeis_); there are oil glands and _ceruminous_, or _wax_, glands in the ear; and special groups of mammals have special glands—for example, the *scent glands* around the anus in the carnivores and between the hooves in the pig.

SCALES

A protective covering of scales is characteristic of a number of vertebrates.

Types of Scales. There are two types of scales: epidermal and dermal.

Epidermal Scales. Epidermal scales are formed from the stratum corneum and hence are particularly characteristic of the animals with a well developed stratum corneum. All of the reptiles and birds are scaly, at least in part, and certain of the mammals have well developed epidermal scales.

Dermal Scales. In contrast to the epidermal scales, dermal scales are developed from mesenchyme in association with the dermis of the skin. They are particularly well developed in the fishes. They are usually in the form of small bony or calcareous plates which may overlap like shingles on a roof or may simply fit closely together. Some animals have both dermal and epidermal scales at the same time.

Comparative Anatomy of Scales. In general, dermal scales are characteristic of the fishes and epidermal scales of the terrestrial amniotes.

Agnatha. No integumentary scales are found in any of the modern cyclostomes. However, the epidermal teeth in the buccal funnel of the cyclostomes represent modified epidermal scales.

Chondrichthyes and Osteichthyes. Epidermal scales are lacking in both the cartilaginous and bony fishes, but dermal scales are particularly well developed in most of them. A few fishes, such as the catfishes and the electric rays, lack scales.

Among the modern fishes, four types of dermal scales are recognized: (1) *placoid scales* are found only in the elasmobranchs, of which the laboratory dogfish is a typical example (see p. 10); (2) *ganoid scales,* which fit together like tiles, rather than overlap like shingles on a roof, are present on *Polypterus* and the gars (*Lepisosteus*) (see p. 12); (3 and 4) *ctenoid* and *cycloid scales,* which do not differ fundamentally in structure and are sometimes both found on the same individual, are characteristic of most of the modern teleost fishes (see p. 12).

Amphibia. The amphibians, being intermediate between the aquatic, pisciform vertebrates on the one hand and the more thoroughly terrestrial amniotes on the other, are likewise intermediate in the condition of their scales. For the most part, they have lost the dermal scales so prominent in the fishes but have not yet gained the highly developed epidermal structures of the amniotes. Minute dermal scales are embedded in the skin of some of the caecilians, and a few toads have bony plates embedded in the skin of the back. Epidermal scales are represented by highly cornified areas (used for digging) on the feet of some of the toads. A few other amphibians have clawlike, cornified, epidermal structures on the tips of the digits. Otherwise, the amphibians are largely scaleless.

Reptilia. Both dermal and epidermal scales occur in the reptiles, but the underlying, bony dermal scales are not as widespread as the overlying, horny epidermal scales. Some of the lizards have dermal scales (osteoderms), and the crocodilians have well developed dermal bony plates along the back. Both the crocodilians and *Sphenodon* possess *gastralia,* which are actually dermal bones developed on the belly side of these animals. (These structures will be discussed with the ribs in Chap. 7.) Turtles have highly developed, bony dermal scales which become intimately associated with the internal skeleton to contribute to the formation of the *carapace* on the turtle's back and the *plastron* on its ventral side.

Epidermal scales are widespread in the reptiles and indeed are a chief diagnostic character of the class as a whole. The epidermal scales of lizards and snakes are folded, one over the other like shingles on a roof, with the free edge of each scale projecting backward. On the other hand, the epidermal scales of the turtles and crocodilians develop separately, and each scale is contiguous with those adjacent to it. The epidermal scales of the turtles not only overlie the carapace and plastron but also cover the soft parts such as the neck and legs. Epidermal scales are ultimately worn away or shed. The shedding process is known as *ecdysis,*

Aves. Dermal scales are lacking among the birds, but epidermal scales are universally present in the group. Most of the epidermal scales of the birds are confined to the legs and feet.

Mammalia. Epidermal scales are present in some of the mammals. They cover the body of the scaly anteater and of the armadillo, but in most mammals in which they are present they are confined to areas on the tail and around the paws. Imbricated epidermal scales are present on the tail of many of the rodents, such as the mouse and rat. These scales are not so strongly cornified as are the scales of the reptiles, nor is there periodic ecdysis. Dermal scales underlie the epidermal scales of the armadillo.

SPECIAL INTEGUMENTARY STRUCTURES

A number of integumentary derivatives are confined to one or a very few groups so that we really cannot discuss their comparative anatomy. However, they are worth mentioning because they do serve to characterize the groups in which they occur.

Feathers. Feathers are highly modified epidermal scales. They are the outstanding feature of birds and are found nowhere else in the animal kingdom. There are three basic types of feathers: *contour feathers* (*plumes*); *down feathers* (*plumules*); and *hair feathers* (*filoplumes*). Contour feathers are the large ones that give the bird its general shape. They consist of a hollow *quill* imbedded in the skin, a long *shaft* or *rachis*, and a broad, flat *vane* composed of *barbs* which extend out from both sides of the shaft. The barbs in turn bear *barbules* which hook together adjacent barbs.

Down feathers are smaller than contour feathers, and the barbs branch out from the free end of the quill. They are found in nestling birds and under the contour feathers of adults. Hair feathers or "pin feathers" have only the shaft with sometimes a small tuft of barbs at the end. They are usually scattered over the body surface, but may be concentrated around the mouth as "whiskers."

Like the epidermal scales of reptiles, the feathers of birds are replaced from time to time. Many birds, particularly those of the temperate and arctic regions, have a seasonal molt in which the feathers are shed and replaced within a few weeks, or the replacement may be more gradual.

Hair. As feathers are unique to the birds, so is hair unique to the mammals. A hair consists of a *root* imbedded in the skin and a projecting *shaft*. While hair is also a modified epidermal structure, its relationship with the reptilian-type epidermal scale is not nearly so clear as with the feather. It should be noted, however, that when scales occur on mammals, they are invariably associated with hairs, and this is one of the reasons for the belief that the mammalian hair was originally derived from an epidermal scale. While the presence of hair is absolutely characteristic of mammals, in many of them it is so reduced that only traces remain. A few coarse hairs in the region of the snout are the only ones found in the adults of some large whales.

Hairs, like feathers, are shed and replaced either gradually or in one or more seasonal molts during the year.

Claws, Nails, and Hooves. Claws, nails, and hooves, the hard structures at the distal ends of the digits of many vertebrates, are cornified derivatives of the integument. They all basically consist of a densely cornified structure, the *unguis*, on the dorsal side of the distal end of the digit; it is joined with the skin on the inner surface of the digit by a softer epidermal derivative, the *subunguis*. Nails, claws, and hooves all grow parallel to the surface of the skin, thus differing from most other epidermal structures. They must either be worn away at the tip or be trimmed at intervals. Claws are present in reptiles, birds, and mammals. Nails and hooves are modified claws found only in certain groups of mammals.

Horns and Antlers. While horns are present in a few lizards, they are otherwise typically mammalian structures. A number of different types of horns and antlers occur among the mammals. Hollow horns, like those found in cattle and buffaloes, are comprised of a cornified layer of epidermis surrounding a central core of bone which projects from the frontal bone of the cranium. This epidermis remains attached to the bony core and increases in size as the animal grows. The horn of the American pronghorn, or prongbuck, as it is sometimes known, differs somewhat from the typical hollow horn of the cow. It also has a central bony core covered with a thick, cornified epidermal layer, but this outer epidermal layer is shed seasonally, although the bony core persists.

Antlers, such as are found in the male members of the deer tribe, are also bony projections from the frontal bone. The newly formed antler is covered with a soft skin which never becomes cornified, and the antler is then said to be "in velvet." When the antler has completed its growth, its blood supply diminishes and the skin dries and cracks and is rubbed off, leaving only the bony core of the antler. Usually in the spring of the year, the bony core in turn becomes loosened and is shed and a new antler develops during the summer. The horn of the rhinoceros differs from the horns of other animals in that it has no bony core but instead is made entirely of agglutinated, modified hairs perched on a roughened area of the nasal bones. It is not shed.

Beaks. Some animals that lack teeth on the jaws (turtles and birds) or have very reduced teeth (trachystomes), have the jawbones covered instead with horny epidermal sheaths to form a beak or bill.

6

Skeletal System

The general pattern of the evolution of the skeletal system among vertebrates has consisted of a shift from a well developed external skeleton primarily concerned with protection to a well developed internal skeleton primarily concerned with support.

ELEMENTS OF THE SKELETON

The vertebrate skeletal system is made up of three kinds of elements: *dermal* or *membrane bones; cartilage;* and *cartilage bones (endochondral* or *chondral bones)*. Where skeletal elements articulate with one another, they form a *joint*.

Membrane Bone. Membrane bones are formed from mesenchymal cells which aggregate where the bone will develop. These cells form an interlacing meshwork of tough connective tissue fibers, and subsequently differentiate into *osteoblasts,* or bone-forming cells, which secrete a matrix. Calcium salts are deposited in this matrix to form real bone. After the meshwork of bony material has been formed, the osteoblasts lay down laminated sheets of compact bone tissue on both the inner and the outer surfaces of the developing bone to form hard inner and outer *tables*. After the bone is formed, the osteoblasts are called *osteocytes. Red bone marrow* develops in the spaces of the original meshwork of bony tissue. The bone is surrounded by a tough sheet of connective tissue, the *periosteum*. Once formed, bone may continue to grow only at its periphery, not by internal expansion.

Membrane bones apparently first evolved as an outer, protective armor developed from the dermis. Scales of fish really represent membrane bones. In the tetrapods, the membrane bones that remain have usually migrated from the skin to become associated with the internal skeleton. These membrane bones include a number of the thin, flattened bones of the skull and the shoulder girdle.

Cartilage. Cartilage is a tough sustentative tissue which also develops from mesenchymal cells. In contrast to bone, it is capable of growth by internal expansion. It is essentially an internal skeletal structure, characteristic of the embryo but also present in the skeleton of the adult.

Cartilage Bone. Cartilage bones are first preformed in cartilage. These masses of cartilage usually are miniature replicas of the bone that will ultimately replace them. The cartilage is destroyed and osteoblast cells form bone tissue in its place. The bone replaces the cartilage as a single unit in many of the short or small bones of the body; thus, the bone forms as a single structure from the beginning. However, some of the long bones of the vertebrates are formed not from a single center of ossification in the cartilage but from three centers. For example, each of the long bones of the mammalian limb forms in three parts: a central *diaphysis* and terminal *epiphyses*. The epiphysis on each end is separated from the diaphysis by a cartilaginous *epiphyseal plate*. So long as the epiphyseal plate remains cartilaginous, the bone continues to elongate. Ultimately, however, the ossification within the epiphysis becomes continuous with the ossification of the end of the diaphysis, and henceforth the bone is one solid structure and can no longer elongate appreciably (Fig. 6-1).

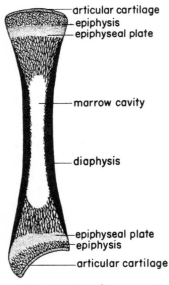

articular cartilage
epiphysis
epiphyseal plate

marrow cavity

diaphysis

epiphyseal plate
epiphysis
articular cartilage

FIG. 6-1. Semidiagrammatic figure of a longitudinal section through a developing long bone. Increase in length takes place mainly in the region of the epiphyseal plates. (After Weichert, *Anatomy of the Chordates,* McGraw-Hill, 1951, by permission.)

Joints. Joints between adjacent bones in the vertebrate skeleton are essentially of two sorts: *synarthroses* are immovable joints such as the sutures of the skull, the symphyses between the pubic bones, and the connections between the diaphysis and epiphyses of a long bone; *diarthroses,* on the other hand, are movable joints. A *synovial cavity* develops between bones in a diarthrodial joint; a *synovial capsule* surrounds the cavity, which is filled with *synovial fluid*. This fluid reduces the friction arising from movement of adjacent bones.

AXIAL SKELETON

The axial skeleton consists of the skull and the vertebral column, with its associated ribs and sternum.

The Skull

The vertebrate skull may be composed entirely of cartilage, or of cartilage and cartilage bones with an investment of dermal bones surrounding them. The cartilage may be more or less completely replaced by bone, and the number of bones may be reduced by loss and fusion. The formation of the skull of any particular vertebrate depends on the degree of progression of this development. Thus, the skull is nothing more than the original mass of cartilage in the hagfishes and Chondrichthyes; it is a central core of chondral bones surrounding the brain and covered by a very extensive development of investing dermal bones in many of the bony fishes; and finally, this dermal investment becomes more and more reduced in the higher tetrapods (Fig. 6-2).

Development of the Skull. In order to understand the evolution, and hence comparative anatomy, of the vertebrate skull, it is essential to comprehend its development.

Formation of Chondrocranium. It is common to speak of the entire cartilaginous portion of the skull as the *chondrocranium* and to differentiate it into the *neurocranium,* which is the portion forming the trough or housing which surrounds the brain, and the *splanchnocranium,* which comprises the visceral cartilages.

Neurocranium. In its earliest stage of development, the vertebrate skull is represented by two pairs of elongated cartilages— a posterior *parachordal* pair and an anterior *prechordal* pair. These paired cartilages are bordered anteriorly by a pair of *nasal capsules,* medially by a pair of *optic capsules,* and posteriorly by

a pair of *otic capsules*. The four elongated cartilages fuse with
one another to form the floor of the original chondrocranium. The
nasal capsules and otic capsules fuse with this floor; the optic
capsules, however, remain separate from it. This floor, or *palate*, of
cartilage under the brain then develops a posterior wall which
grows up to surround the nerve cord as it leaves the brain. The
opening through which the nerve cord passes is the *foramen
magnum*. Lateral walls also grow up on either side of the brain.

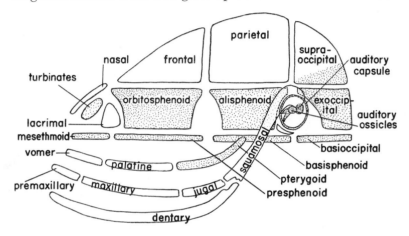

Fig. 6-2. A diagrammatic lateral view of a mammalian skull. Cartilage
bones stippled, dermal bones clear. The palatine, as shown here, is a
dermal bone that has invested the anterior end of the palatopterygoquadrate
cartilage. The unstippled portion of the supraoccipital represents the interparietal bone, a dermal bone which has become fused to the supraoccipital,
a cartilage bone. (Modified after Flower.)

SPLANCHNOCRANIUM. A series of *visceral cartilages* support the
visceral arches which separate the pharyngeal pouches. The first
arch (*mandibular*) on each side lies anterior to the first pouch and
is supported by two cartilages: a dorsal *palatopterygoquadrate
bar* and a ventral *Meckel's cartilage*. The dorsal cartilage contributes to the formation of the upper jaw while the ventral
cartilage forms the core of the lower jaw. The cartilages of the
second visceral arch (the *hyoid*) comprise a dorsal *hyomandibular,* a median *ceratohyal,* and a ventral *basihyal*. Each of the remaining five visceral arches consists of five separate cartilages
which are (from dorsal to ventral), the *pharyngobranchial, epi-*

branchial, ceratobranchial, hypobranchial, and *basibranchial* cartilages. In the tetrapods, the visceral cartilages largely disappear, but portions of them persist to form the *hyoid apparatus* which supports the tongue, and the cartilages of the larynx.

Chondral Bones. A number of separate centers of ossification form in the original chondrocranium.

NEUROCRANIAL OSSIFICATIONS. The occipital bones develop from the posterior wall of the chondrocranium. These four bones (a dorsal *supraoccipital,* two lateral *exoccipitals,* and a ventral *basioccipital*) surround the foramen magnum. The occipitals may fuse to form a single *occipital bone.*

The floor of the original chondrocranium may ossify posteriorly to form the *basisphenoid,* medially to form the *presphenoid,* and anteriorly to form *ethmoid* elements. The lateral wall of the chondrocranium may ossify posteriorly to give rise to the *alisphenoid bone,* and adjacent to the optic capsule to give rise to the *orbitosphenoid* elements.

The nasal capsule becomes associated with and gives rise to *ethmoid* elements. The optic capsule may give rise to *optic cartilages* or, in some of the turtles and birds, to *scleral bones.* The otic capsule may ossify to form a series of *otic bones* surrounding the inner ear: the *pro-otic,* forming the anterior housing of the ear; the *epiotic,* forming the roof of the housing of the ear; and the *opisthotic,* forming the posterior wall of the housing of the ear. In later development these otic bones may fuse to form a single *periotic bone,* which in turn, in the higher vertebrates, develops into the *petrosal bone.*

SPLANCHNOCRANIAL OSSIFICATIONS. The posterior end of the palatopterygoquadrate cartilage ossifies to form the *quadrate bone,* and the posterior end of Meckel's cartilage ossifies to form the *articular bone.* The hyomandibular gives rise to the *columella* of the amphibians, which ultimately forms the *stapes* of the ear of the higher vertebrates.

Dermal Investing Bones. All other bones of the vertebrate skull form as investing dermal bones surrounding some portion of the chondral skull. These bones can generally be divided into four basic groups: a series of paired roofing bones forming the roof of the cranium; paired marginal bones forming the walls of the cranium; medial palatal bones forming a floor underneath the cranium; and a series of dermal bones surrounding the anterior elements of the original splanchnocranium. Together these dermal investing bones are referred to as the *dermatocranium*.

ROOFING BONES. The more important roofing bones include a series of paired bones on the dorsal surface of the skull: the *nasals, frontals,* and *parietals.* Sometimes a median, single *interparietal* bone may develop. Since this bone is characteristic of the Inca Indians of Peru, it is sometimes known as the *Inca bone.* In the posterolateral angle of the skull are found the *supratemporal, squamosal,* and *tabular* bones. Bones of the orbital wall include the *lacrimal* and *orbital* bones.

MARGINAL BONES. The paired marginal bones forming the wall of the skull are (from anterior to posterior) the *premaxillaries, maxillaries, jugals,* and *quadratojugals.*

PALATAL BONES. Underneath, forming a floor under the chondral elements are (from anterior to posterior) the paired *vomers,* an unpaired *parasphenoid,* the paired *palatines,* and the paired *pterygoids.*

In the higher vertebrates, a secondary bony palate develops beneath the primary palate which forms the floor of the brain case. This secondary palate divides the original mouth cavity into an upper *nasal chamber* and a lower *oral chamber.* When a secondary palate is formed, it develops from elements of the premaxillaries, the maxillaries, and the palatines. In the crocodilians, the pterygoids also contribute to the development of this palate.

TABLE 1

DERMAL BONES THAT INVEST MECKEL'S CARTILAGE
IN THE MODERN VERTEBRATES

Osteichthyes	Amphibia	Reptiles and Birds	Mammals
Dentary Angular Derm-articular	Dentary Prearticular Coronoid	Dentary Angular Surangular Derm-articular Splenial Prearticular Coronoid (not in birds)	Dentary

DERMAL BONES SURROUNDING SPLANCHNOCRANIUM. The dermal elements surrounding Meckel's cartilage include such bones as the *dentary,* the *angular,* the *surangular,* the *splenial,* and the *coronoid* (Table 1). The palatines and pterygoids, which surround the anterior end of the palatopterygoquadrate cartilage, are fused with the rest of the cranium and hence were included with the palatal bones mentioned above.

BONES OF OPERCULUM. In the bony fishes, additional dermal bones (the *opercular,* the *preopercular,* and the *subopercular*) develop as paired bones which support the flaps covering the openings of the gill chambers.

Comparative Anatomy of the Skull. The evolution and comparative anatomy of the vertebrate skull is simply a history of the various elements discussed above.

Agnatha. The chondrocranium of the cyclostomes is a cartilaginous housing around the brain and a basket-like meshwork of cartilage surrounding the pharynx. No bone is present.

Chondrichthyes. All of the Chondrichthyes have a chondrocranium more or less like that seen in the laboratory animal, the spiny dogfish (*Squalus acanthias*). Usually the palatopterygoquadrate cartilage, which forms the upper jaw, is suspended from the skull by the hyomandibular cartilage of the second visceral arch—a *hyostylic* jaw. In the chimeras, however, the palatopterygoquadrate is fused to the chondrocranium—an *autostylic* jaw. No bone is present in the skull of the cartilaginous fishes.

Osteichthyes. Considerable variation in skull structure is found among the bony fishes. The chondrocranium remains unossified in the Chondrostei, though some dermal bones are present. In the other fishes (the Holostei, Teleostei, and Choanichthyes) the chondrocranium is more or less ossified and numerous dermal bones are present. Usually the jaw attachment of fishes is hyostylic, but autostylic jaws are found in the lungfishes and the chondrostean *Polypterus.*

Amphibia. The primitive amphibians had numerous dermal bones which formed a large, boxlike housing surrounding the brain, but elements of the dermatocranium are reduced in the modern amphibians and numerous openings or vacuities have developed in the skull. Chondral ossifications are also reduced so that much cartilage is present in the skull. The amphibians have lost the opercular bones of the fishes. The jaw is invariably autostylic, as it is in all tetrapods; hence, the original hyomandibular no longer has a suspensory function. It now forms the columella of the middle ear which appears for the first time in the amphibians.

The skull of the modern amphibian articulates with the first vertebra by a pair of prominences on the exoccipital bones—the *occipital condyles.*

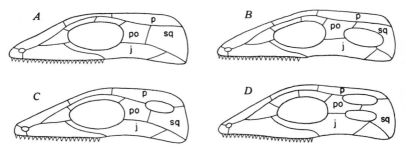

Fig. 6-3. Diagram showing the temporal openings in the different types of reptile skulls. *A*, anapsid; *B*, synapsid; *C*, parapsid; *D*, diapsid; p, parietal; po, postorbital; sq, squamosal; j, jugal. (Redrawn from Romer, A.S.: *The Vertebrate Body.* Ed. 3. Philadelphia: W. B. Saunders Company, 1962.)

Reptilia. Skulls of reptiles, as of the other amniotes, are well ossified, with little cartilage remaining. The primitive reptiles, like the primitive amphibians, had boxlike skulls, but in the skulls of modern reptiles openings bounded by arches of bone have developed. There are basically four types of reptilian skulls. The *anapsid* type has no additional openings in the skull other than the original nasal, eye, and ear openings. (This is the primitive type, found in modern reptiles only among the turtles.) In the *synapsid* type an opening develops along the lateral side of the skull, leaving a lower, or *zygomatic,* arch. (This type of skull is found in the line of reptiles that gave rise to the mammals.) The *parapsid* type has openings developed dorsolaterally on the posterior portion of the skull. (Reptiles with this type of skull became marine and gave rise to the ichthyosaurs and plesiosaurs.) Finally, in the *diapsid* type both dorsal and lateral openings develop on the posterior portion of the skull. The great majority of all reptiles, both living and extinct, have diapsid skulls. (Fig. 6-3.)

All modern reptiles have only a single, median, occipital condyle.

Aves. The birds are essentially similar to the diapsid reptiles. A single occipital condyle is present. The bones investing Meckel's cartilage begin to unite. In addition, *sclerotic bones*, which surround and protect the eye, develop from the original otic capsule.

Mammalia. All of the mammals developed from a synapsid stock of reptiles, and hence all have the lateral opening and a more or less developed zygomatic arch. Two occipital condyles are present. Compared with the skulls of the lower vertebrates, the mammalian skull shows a marked reduction in the number of dermal elements. This reduction results largely from the fusion of dermal bones with each other and also with chondral bones. Fusion has taken place not only in the cranium proper but also in the mandible. Thus, the only bone remaining in the mandible of a mammal is the dentary, while the dermal elements of the lower jaw of a reptile, for example, include the dentary, angular, surangular, splenial, and coronoid bones.

With the reduction of the lower jaw of the mammal to a single bony element, the dentary, there has been a shift in function of two other bones—the quadrate and the articular. In the original mandibular arch the upper jaw articulated with the lower jaw by the posterior ends of the palatopterygoquadrate cartilage and Meckel's cartilage. When chondral bones were formed, the posterior end of the former became the *quadrate* and the posterior end of the latter, the *articular*. Thus, the lower jaw of amphibians and reptiles is joined to the skull by means of an articulation between the quadrate of the skull and the articular of the lower jaw. With the formation of the more highly developed middle ear of the mammals, the quadrate became modified to form the *incus* of the mammalian middle ear while the modified articular bone became the *malleus*. Hence, the lower jaw could no longer articulate with the cranium by means of an articular-quadrate connection. A new articulation, the dentary to the squamosal, developed; this type of jaw articulation is unique to the mammals.

Teeth. Teeth may appropriately be discussed with three different systems: with the integument because it is here that their homologies lie; with the digestive system because it is here that their functions lie; or with the skeleton because it is here that they are structurally located. Since our primary concern is anatomy, we shall discuss the teeth at this point as they are structurally part of the skull.

Among the vertebrates, teeth are used primarily for the purpose of capturing or holding prey. They may be subsequently modified for use as cutting, crushing, or grinding organs.

Types of Teeth. Two types of teeth occur in the vertebrates: *epidermal* teeth and *true* teeth.

EPIDERMAL TEETH. Epidermal teeth are nothing more than cornified epithelial projections and are not in any way homologous to true teeth. The distribution of epidermal teeth among the living vertebrates is quite limited. They are perhaps best developed among the cyclostomes which lack true teeth, and may be found along the edges of the jaws of most larval frogs and toads. They are found along the edge of the "bill" of the duckbill platypus (*Ornithorhynchus*). The sheets of "whalebone" or baleen in the mouths of some whales are also derived from cornified epidermal papillae.

TRUE TEETH. Most vertebrates have true teeth. They vary widely in shape, but all are built on the same fundamental plan which is not too unlike that of the homologous placoid scale of the spiny shark. The exterior portion of the tooth, the *crown,* is covered with *enamel.* Under the crown lies a softer portion of *dentine,* in the center of which is a *pulp cavity.* The development of the tooth is the same throughout the vertebrates. The enamel is derived from ectoderm, whereas the rest of the tooth is derived from the dermal mesenchyme. The teeth may be restricted to the jawbones, or they may also be present on the roof of the mouth, the tongue, and even the visceral arches.

There are various patterns of succession, attachment, and differentiation that true teeth may follow.

Succession. In some vertebrates the teeth are constantly replaced throughout life, whereas others have a restricted number of sets of teeth. Thus, the individual teeth of the dogfish (*Squalus*) are shed and replaced an indefinite number of times during the life of the animal, a condition referred to as *polyphyodont.* The teeth of the higher vertebrates are replaced in successive waves which progress from the anterior portion of the jaw to the posterior portion. The teeth may still be polyphyodont, as in the crocodilians. Mammals have fewer waves of tooth replacement than other vertebrates. Most mammals are *diphyodont,* that is, only two waves of teeth are formed. The first wave is the *milk dentition,* the second the *permanent dentition.* Some mammals, such as the cetaceans, are *monophyodont*, having but a single set of teeth throughout life.

Attachment. The method by which the teeth are attached to the jaw varies. The tooth may sit on the edge of the jaw, an *acrodont* tooth; it may be attached to a shelf on the inner margin of the jaw, a *pleurodont* tooth; or it may be held in a socket in the jawbone, a *thecodont* tooth.

Differentiation. If the teeth are more or less uniform in shape, each tooth being similar to its neighbors, the dentition is said to be *homodont*. If the teeth are differentiated into various types (e.g., incisors, canines, molars) the dentition is *heterodont*.

Comparative Anatomy of Vertebrate Teeth. In general, the history of the evolution of vertebrate teeth has entailed a reduction in number and a restriction of location to the jawbones.

AGNATHA. Only epidermal teeth are present in the cyclostomes. The lamprey has a series of epidermal teeth on the inner wall of the buccal funnel. The hagfish has a single, median tooth lying above the mouth opening; its remaining epidermal teeth are located only on the tongue.

CHONDRICHTHYES. The teeth of the laboratory animal, the spiny dogfish (*Squalus*) are typical of the Chondrichthyes. Restricted to the jaws, they are polyphyodont, acrodont, and homodont. Some Chondrichthyes have a number of teeth modified to form crushing plates and thus may have heterodont teeth.

OSTEICHTHYES. Some of the bony fishes are toothless as adults (e.g., sea horses and sturgeons), but teeth are present in most fishes and are usually polyphyodont, acrodont, and homodont. A few fishes have thecodont dentition and a number of teleosts are heterodont. There is considerable variation in the number and particularly in the location of the teeth; some fishes have them only on the jaws, but many others have teeth on bones of the roof of the mouth, on the tongue, and even on the visceral arches.

AMPHIBIA. Larval frogs and toads have epidermal teeth. With this exception, the teeth of amphibians are true teeth. Although most frogs lack teeth on the lower jaw, one South American form does have true teeth on the mandible. The teeth of amphibians, while not so widely distributed as those of the bony fishes, occur in various locations besides the jawbones; they may be present on the palatines, the vomers, the pterygoids, and even the parasphenoid. Teeth are lacking in the toads (*Bufo*) and aquatic frogs of the genus *Pipa*. Amphibian teeth are acrodont, polyphyodont, and usually homodont.

REPTILIA. All reptiles except the turtles have teeth. Snakes and lizards may have them on the pterygoids and palatines as well as on the jawbones. *Sphenodon* has vomerine teeth. Crocodilians have teeth only on the jaws. Typically among the reptiles the teeth are polyphyodont and homodont, but there is variation as to method of attachment. They are generally either acrodont or pleurodont in the snakes and lizards. The crocodilians have a true thecodont dentition. Some of the extinct reptiles had well developed heterodont teeth, and a few of the modern forms approach this condition. The poison fangs of certain snakes and the Gila monster are modified true teeth.

AVES. All modern birds are toothless. *Archaeopteryx* had thecodont teeth, and in *Hesperornis* the teeth were set in a continuous groove in the jawbone.

MAMMALIA. The adult duckbill platypus (*Ornithorhynchus*) lacks true teeth. It does have epidermal teeth, and a single set of true teeth appears during embryonic development but is soon lost. Apparently no teeth are present at any time in the spiny anteater, *Tachyglossus* (*Echidna*). In placental mammals, only certain anteaters and the whalebone whales lack true teeth. Mammalian teeth are thecodont.

Most mammals are diphyodont or nearly so. A few mammals have only a single set of teeth in their lifetime and hence are monophyodont. Humans are nearly, but not quite, diphyodont; the molars represent the posterior portion of the first set of teeth (the milk dentition), while the incisors, canines, and premolars of the adult represent the incomplete wave of the second set.

The toothed whales are homodont; the other mammals that have true teeth are heterodont, although the teeth may not be sharply differentiated. The tooth row normally comprises anterior *incisors*, behind these a single *canine*, posterior to these the *premolars*, and finally *molars*. One or more of these types may be lacking. In some mammals *carnassial* teeth, which are formed especially for shearing, develop in each jaw from a premolar above and a molar below. The number and kinds of teeth are usually indicated by a *dental formula* showing the number of incisors, canines, premolars, and molars in the upper and lower jaw on one side. Thus, the dental formula of man is:

$$I \frac{2}{2}, C \frac{1}{1}, P \frac{2}{2}, M \frac{3}{3}$$

Vertebral Column

The vertebral column, formed as it is of separate blocks, the vertebrae, gives protection to the spinal cord and at the same time remains flexible enough to allow for movement of the parts of the body. The processes of the vertebrae provide surfaces for muscle attachment. The vertebrae develop around the notochord from the sclerotomes (Fig. 6-4).

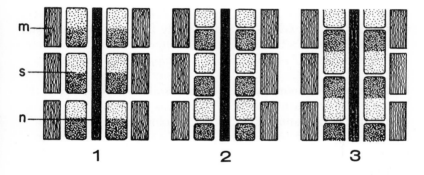

Fig. 6-4. Diagram showing the relationship of notochord (n), sclerotome (s), and myotome (m) in the development of the vertebrate. The anterior part of one sclerotome fuses to the posterior portion of the sclerotome anterior to it so that the sclerotomes come to alternate with the myotomes. 1, early stage; 2, intermediate stage; 3, final stage.

Structure of a Vertebra. A vertebra typically consists of a central, massive, weight-supporting portion, the *centrum,* above which rises an arch surrounding the *neural canal* through which the spinal cord passes. This neural arch terminates dorsally in the *neural spine.* Sometimes a ventral *hemal arch* develops around blood vessels lying beneath the vertebral column.

Centrum. There is some variation in shape of the centra, both within a single vertebral column and between the vertebrae of different kinds of animals. Sometimes the centrum is concave both anteriorly and posteriorly; it is said to be *amphicoelous*. The centrum may be concave anteriorly but convex posteriorly; such a vertebra is a *procoelous* one. Sometimes the centrum is concave posteriorly but convex anteriorly, an *opisthocoelous* vertebra. And sometimes, as in the mammals, the centrum may be nearly flat on both the anterior and posterior surfaces, the *amphiplatyan* or *acoelous* condition.

Vertebral Processes. Various processes known as *apophyses* may project from the vertebra. A pair of *prezygapophyses,* one on each side, may project anteriorly from the neural arch to articulate with the *postygapophyses* which project posteriorly from the vertebra in front; thus the vertebrae articulate at three points: at their centra and at the two pairs of zygapophyses. The vertebra may also have various paired *transverse processes:* the *diapophyses,* which project laterally from the base of the neural arch; the *parapophyses,* which project laterally from the centrum; and the *basapophyses,* which project ventrolaterally from the centrum. A median, ventrally-projecting *hypapophysis* may be present.

Comparative Anatomy of the Vertebral Column. During the course of vertebrate evolution, there was a marked increase in regional differentiation of the vertebral column.

Agnatha. The hagfishes are unique among the vertebrates in that they lack any vertebral elements whatsoever, the notochord being the only supporting structure. In the lampreys, on the other hand, cartilaginous blocks which develop alongside the notochord represent incompletely developed vertebrae.

Chondrichthyes. The vertebrae of the Chondrichthyes are similar throughout to those seen in the dogfish. The individual vertebra is entirely cartilaginous and amphicoelous, and it has a neural arch and spine developed dorsally. In the caudal region, a hemal arch surrounds the caudal artery and vein. Thus the column is divided into two regions: one area contains *dorsal vertebrae* without hemal arches, and the other region comprises *caudal vertebrae* with hemal arches.

Osteichthyes. Vertebrae of the Osteichthyes are typically bony and amphicoelous, with dorsal neural arches and spines, as well as (in the caudal region) hemal arches and spines. Each centrum in the caudal region of the primitive holostean, *Amia,* is divided into an anterior and a posterior segment.

Amphibia. Among the amphibians several advances appear in the vertebral column. The vertebrae for the first time differentiate into four regions instead of two. In addition to the *trunk* vertebrae (dorsals) and caudal vertebrae seen in the Chondrichthyes and Osteichthyes, the anterior amphibian vertebra which articulates with the cranium differentiates as a *cervical* vertebra, and at least one vertebra at the posterior end of the row of dorsals articulates with the pelvic girdle to become a true *sacral* vertebra. In the frogs and toads the caudal vertebrae are replaced by a long rod of bone, the *urostyle*. The vertebrae of amphibians also develop zygapophyses both anteriorly and posteriorly. Transverse processes are also present. Amphicoelous, procoelous, and opisthocoelous vertebrae are found within the group; sometimes more than one kind are present in an individual.

Reptilia. Further differentiation of the vertebral column takes place in the reptiles. In contrast to the single cervical of the amphibians, the first two vertebrae are differentiated into a definitive *atlas* and *axis,* and usually these are followed by a series of additional cervical vertebrae. The dorsal vertebrae may be more or less uniform throughout their length, but in the crocodilians they differentiate into *thoracic* vertebrae with ribs and *lumbar* vertebrae without ribs. When sacral vertebrae are present, there are always at least two of them in the reptiles. Thus the reptilian column is divided into cervical, dorsal, sacral, and caudal regions, or, in the crocodilians, into cervical, thoracic, lumbar, sacral, and caudal regions.

The snakes and a few of the lizards develop additional articulating surfaces between adjacent vertebrae. The *zygosphene* on either side of the anterior face of the vertebra projects into and articulates with the inner wall of a cavity, the *zygantrum,* on the posterior face of the vertebra anterior to it. Thus, each vertebra has five surfaces which articulate with the preceding vertebra: the centrum, two zygapophyses, and two zygosphenes.

All types of centra are found in the reptiles.

Aves. Differentiation of the vertebral column of the birds is essentially similar to that of the reptiles. However, a good bit of fusion takes place. The thoracics tend to fuse to form a single structure. The last thoracic vertebra, the lumbars, the sacrals, and a few anterior caudals are fused with the enlarged ilia of the pelvic girdle to form a single solid structure, the *synsacrum.* In

most birds the posterior caudal vertebrae are fused to form the
pygostyle which supports the tail feathers. The birds do not have
zygosphenes and zygantra, but they have well developed zygapophyses. The centra in the neck region of most modern birds are
saddle-shaped; the anterior face is convex dorsoventrally and
concave from side to side, and the posterior face curves in the
opposite direction. Vertebrae with centra of this shape are called
heterocoelous.

Mammalia. The mammals have well developed cervical vertebrae with an atlas and axis, well developed thoracic and lumbar
vertebrae, at least three fused sacral vertebrae, and a series of
caudal vertebrae. Zygapophyses are prominent. In both the birds
and the mammals, small costal (rib) elements fuse with the sides
of the cervical vertebrae so that a series of small openings—the
foramina transversaria—are formed. Certain blood vessels pass
through these openings on their way to the head. Mammalian
vertebrae are typically amphiplatyan.

Ribs and Sternum

Ribs are elongated cartilaginous or bony elements which develop in the myocommata of the body wall and are associated
with the vertebrae. Originally they served simply as places for
muscle attachment, but in the higher forms they become part of
a *thoracic basket*—a strong, protective cage formed in the thoracic
region by the ribs and the ventral *sternum* or *breastbone*.

Ribs. Two types of ribs have developed among the vertebrates:
dorsal ribs, which are associated with the diapophyses and which
extend out through the lateral septum that separates the dorsal
and ventral muscle masses of the trunk; and *ventral ribs*, which
are associated with the basapophyses and which extend around
the inner wall of the coelomic cavity.

In the fishes, ventral ribs are the most common, although some
fishes do have dorsal ribs as well. The tetrapods have only dorsal
ribs, which are frequently two-headed (*bicipital*). If present in
the amphibians, the ribs fail to reach the sternum and simply
extend for some distance through the lateral septum. They are
reduced or absent in the frogs. Among the reptiles, the ribs of
the turtle are greatly modified to form part of the bony carapace
which protects the animal. (The crocodilians and *Sphenodon*

also have so-called "belly ribs" or *gastralia,* which help support the body wall in the ventral abdominal region. These are dermal bones, not chondral as are the true ribs.) Birds have special *uncinate processes* extending from one rib to another for bracing purposes.

Sternum. The sternum is a tetrapod structure consisting of one or several cartilaginous or bony elements in the ventral thoracic region. It first appears as mesenchymal strands in certain salamanders, in which it has no connection whatsoever with the ribs. The sternal elements of the frog become associated with the pectoral girdle, and finally, in the amniotes, the sternum is joined to the ribs proper. The sternum of birds is very large and well ossified and, in most birds, has a prominent *keel* for the attachment of flight muscles.

APPENDICULAR SKELETON

The appendicular skeleton comprises the pectoral girdle, the pelvic girdle, and the paired appendages. The girdles are located within the trunk; they serve for the attachment and support of the paired appendages and of the muscles which move the fins or limbs.

Pectoral Girdle. The pectoral girdle supports the anterior pair of appendages.

Elements of Pectoral Girdle. The pectoral girdle may be composed of both chondral and dermal elements. Chondral elements which may be involved in its formation are (on each side) the ventral *coracoid* and the dorsal *scapula* and *suprascapula.* Dermal bones which may be present are (on each side) a ventral *clavicle* which lies anterior to the coracoid, and, dorsal to the clavicle, a *cleithrum* and a *supracleithrum.*

Comparative Anatomy of Pectoral Girdle. The chondral part of the pectoral girdle is the more important of the two components since it forms the *glenoid fossa* in which the fore limb articulates. The dermal elements are reduced in the tetrapods.

AGNATHA. The cyclostomes have no pectoral girdle elements of any sort.

CHONDRICHTHYES. Among the Chondrichthyes, obviously, there can be no dermal elements, since the entire skeleton is cartilaginous. The pectoral girdle is composed of a single U-shaped *scapulocoracoid cartilage* with a suprascapular cartilage attached to the free (dorsal) edge of each scapular process.

OSTEICHTHYES. Among the bony fishes, the coracoid and scapula are usually present as chondral bones, and the clavicle, cleithrum, and supracleithrum are usually present as dermal bones. A *posttemporal* bone above the supracleithrum may attach the pectoral girdle to the skull. The various cleithral elements are not present in the classes higher than the bony fishes.

AMPHIBIA. The dermal bones are lacking in the Caudata; the coracoid, scapula, and suprascapula are the only elements present. In the Anura, the coracoid, scapula, suprascapula, and the *epicoracoid cartilages* (between the coracoids) represent the chondral elements. The only dermal bone present is the clavicle.

REPTILIA. Among the reptiles, the chondral elements are represented by the coracoid, scapula, and suprascapula. The dermal bones are reduced. The clavicle may be present and small in size or it may be absent, as in the crocodilians and some of the legless lizards. The clavicles of the turtle become involved in the formation of the plastron.

AVES. The chondral bones (coracoid, scapula, and suprascapula) are present in the birds. The dermal clavicles of the flying birds fuse to form a V-shaped *furcula* or "wishbone." The flightless birds lack a true furcula, since the clavicles do not fuse.

MAMMALIA. Some variation in the pectoral girdle exists among the mammals. In the monotremes it is reptile-like, with the three chondral elements and the clavicle. In the other mammals, the reptilian coracoid has disappeared as a separate bone and the girdle is usually made up of scapula and clavicle. There is some variation in the clavicle in different groups: it may be well developed and strongly attached to the ribs and sternum; it may be reduced in size and completely inarticulated; or it may be absent entirely.

Pelvic Girdle. The pelvic girdle supports the posterior paired appendages.

Elements of Pelvic Girdle. The pelvic girdle includes no dermal bones, being made up entirely of chondral elements.

Comparative Anatomy of Pelvic Girdle. The pelvic girdle is small and relatively unimportant in fishes; it is better developed in the tetrapods in which it must support the weight of the body on land.

AGNATHA. Cyclostomes lack a pelvic girdle.

CHONDRICHTHYES. The pelvic girdle of the Chondrichthyes is made up of paired, cartilaginous *ischiopubic bars,* which fuse to form a single structure and which articulate with the fins but not with the vertebral column.

OSTEICHTHYES. Among the Osteichthyes, bony ischiopubic bars are present and articulate with the pelvic fins. In a few fishes the pelvic girdle may move anteriorly to articulate with the cleithrum.

AMPHIBIA. The pelvic elements of all the tetrapods comprise fundamentally three pairs of bones. On each side there is an anteroventral *pubis,* a posteroventral *ischium,* and a dorsal *ilium.* These may remain as separate bony elements, or they may fuse into a single structure on each side, the *innominate bone.* The cavity formed where the three bones meet for the articulation of the limb is the *acetabulum.*

The pelvic girdle of the Caudata is largely cartilaginous, and in some of them a ventral, forward-projecting *ypsiloid cartilage* is present. The pelvic girdle of the Anura is better ossified, except for the pubis. The elongated ilia articulate with the sacral verte-bra.

REPTILIA. The reptile pelvic girdle is fairly typical for the tetrapods but articulates always with at least two sacral verte-brae (instead of only one, as in the amphibians).

AVES. As mentioned above (p. 69), the ilia of the pelvic girdle are enlarged and become fused with the vertebrae to form a part of the synsacrum. The pubes are reduced.

MAMMALIA. In the mammals the enlarged ilium (the *hipbone*) is fused with the ischium and pubis to form a single innominate bone.

Paired Appendages. Typically the vertebrates have two pairs of appendages, called *fins* in the fishes and *limbs* in the tetrapods. One or both pairs may be reduced or absent.

Fins. Paired appendages are lacking in the Cyclostomata. The chondrichthyian fin is supported by a proximal row of one to five cartilaginous elements called *basalia,* and several distal rows of small *radialia* from which the dermal fin rays extend. In the Actinopterygii, the skeletal elements are reduced and the fin is comprised largely of skin stiffened by horny fin rays. The fin of the Choanichthyes has a median axis of bony elements, some of which are thought to be homologous with bones of the tetrapod limb.

Fishes also have median, unpaired fins—the dorsal, anal, and caudal fins—supported largely by fin rays.

Tetrapod Limb. The tetrapod limb is rather uniform in structure throughout the group.

ELEMENTS OF THE TETRAPOD LIMB. The basic elements are: an upper limb bone, the *humerus* in the fore limb, the *femur* in the hind limb; and a pair of lower limb bones, namely, the *radius* and *ulna* in the fore limb and the *tibia* and *fibula* in the hind limb. Distal to these lower bones in the fore limb is a series of three rows of *carpals,* comprising in the first row the *radiale, intermedium,* and *ulnare.* The second row consists of the *centralia,* and the third row of the *carpalia.* The corresponding *tarsal* bones of the hind limb are the *tibiale, intermedium,* and *fibulare* in the proximal row, then a row of centralia, and finally a row of *tarsalia.* Distal to the carpals and tarsals, respectively, lie the *metacarpals* and *metatarsals* (bones of the hand and foot), and finally the *phalanges* (the bones of the digits). The basic number of digits is five; hence the tetrapod limb is sometimes called the *pentadactyl limb.*

MODIFICATIONS OF THE TETRAPOD LIMB. Most of the modification in the tetrapod limb involves either a fusion or a loss of parts (particularly in the carpus, tarsus, manus, and pes) or a modification of shape to suit a function such as swimming or flying.

The limb is fairly typical in most of the amphibians, although there has been some reduction in the number of elements. The Apoda lack limbs and limb girdles. Trachystomes are without hind limbs and have only two or three digits on the front limbs, and in some of the salamanders the number of toes may be reduced to as few as two. Most reptiles have five toes, although they are reduced to two in some of the lizards and, of course, in some lizards and most snakes the limbs are absent. Among the birds the number of digits on the anterior limb is typically three, and on the posterior limb typically four. Many mammals likewise show reduction of the digits. The cloven-hoofed artiodactyls may have only two digits, while the perissodactyls have either three digits or, in the horse-like animals, only one digit.

HETEROTOPIC BONES

In addition to all of the bones above, certain bones may develop in various soft parts of the body of some animals. Such bones, which seemingly have little relation with the rest of the skeleton, are called *heterotopic bones*. They are most common in the mammals but do occur in some of the lower vertebrates. Among the mammals, familiar examples are the heart bone of the deer, the rostral bone in the snout of the pig, the marsupial bone supporting the pouch in the opossum and its relatives, the diaphragm bone in the camels, the baculum or os penis in the penis of the male of many mammals, and occasionally an os clitoris in the homologue of the penis, the clitoris, of the female.

7

Muscular System

Muscle tissue has the ability to contract in response to stimuli. As we have pointed out (p. 30), there are three main types of muscle tissue: striated, smooth, and cardiac.

Striated (voluntary) muscle tissue is generally gathered into discrete bundles, the muscles, which are covered by sheets of connective tissue, *fascia*. These muscles are under voluntary control. By the contraction of the muscles, the parts of the body are moved in relation to one another. Locomotion, breathing, and seizing and swallowing food are among the many functions performed by the aid of the striated muscles.

Smooth (involuntary) muscle fibers are usually organized into layers that take part in forming the walls of the various tubes, ducts, and blood vessels of the body. They are not under voluntary control and they contract more slowly than do the striated muscles. By their contractions, they change the diameter of the tubes and thereby facilitate and control the movement of substances within the body.

Cardiac muscle, which forms the wall of the heart, is a special type of involuntary muscle tissue which has become striated in appearance.

DEVELOPMENT OF MUSCLES

The majority of the functional muscles of the body are derived from two embryonic sources. Muscles of the first group are called *myotomal* or *skeletal muscles* because they are derived from the the myotome of the epimere and are primarily associated with movements of the skeleton. Muscles of the second group are called *hypomeric muscles;* they are derived from the splanchnic hypomere and most of them are associated with the viscera.

Myotomal Muscles. As the vertebrate embryo develops, the epimere divides into segmentally arranged somites, each of which differentiates into three discrete parts: the _sclerotome_, the _derma-tome_, and the _myotome_ (see p. 39). As shown in Figure 6-4 (p. 67), the sclerotome blocks, from which the vertebrae develop, become rearranged to alternate with the myotomes, from which the basic trunk and limb musculature develops. Hence, the myotomal muscles are basically arranged so that they run from one vertebra to another. The segmental myotomes are separated one from another by sheets of connective tissue, the _myosepta_ or _mycommata_. Myotomal muscles are, without exception, striated in appearance and voluntary in function.

Hypomeric Muscles. Muscle tissue derived from the splanchnic hypomere is associated with the visceral organs and blood vessels and with the splanchnocranium and its derivatives. The visceral musculature is not segmented; for the most part it comprises the sheets of smooth muscle fibers referred to above. However, hypomeric muscles associated with the splanchnocranium and its derivatives take on secondarily a voluntary function, become striated in appearance, and are organized in bundles as are the myotomal muscles. Since the splanchnocranium is actually a skeletal structure surrounding the anterior portion of the gut, it is only logical that visceral muscles should be associated with it.

EVOLUTION OF MYOTOMAL MUSCLES

Since the myotomes from which they are derived are seg-mented, the skeletal muscles tend to be serially arranged.

Trunk Musculature. The trunk musculature and its derivatives, the limb muscles, make up the great bulk of voluntary skeletal muscles of the vertebrate body.

Agnatha. The trunk musculature of the cyclostomes is made up of nearly vertical bands of myotomal muscles, one for each body segment. These muscles are usually simple and undifferentiated, since no appendicular or other special sets of muscles are derived from them.

Chondrichthyes and Osteichthyes. In the fishes, the myotomes of the trunk region become divided into dorsal and ventral sec-tions. The sections in the dorsal region form the _epaxial muscle mass_ and those in the ventral regions the _hypaxial muscle mass_.

These two masses are separated by a horizontal *lateral septum* of connective tissue. Correlated with this division of the trunk musculature into epaxial and hypaxial regions is a modification of the spinal nerves which divide into dorsal and ventral rami. The dorsal ramus of each nerve innervates the epaxial muscle mass, and the ventral ramus innervates the hypaxial muscle mass. The epaxial muscles are rather prominent in the cartilaginous and bony fishes which use them for swimming movements. As we go further up the vertebrate scale there is a pronounced tendency for the epaxial muscles to become less prominent and the hypaxial to become more prominent.

Amphibia. The hypaxial masses of the salamanders become delaminated into four rather distinct layers: the *superficial external oblique;* the *deep external oblique,* the *internal oblique;* and the *transversus.* The *rectus abdominis* differentiates as a median, ventral, longitudinal muscle mass in the amphibians and persists in all the higher vertebrates. The epaxial muscle mass of the amphibians is reduced to some longitudinal muscles along the vertebral column, of which the *dorsalis trunci* is the most important element.

Reptilia. In the reptiles the epaxial mass differentiates into smaller units but still remains essentially the minor group of trunk muscles. The hypaxial muscles become modified by the introduction of the encircling ribs. In the abdominal region of most reptiles the oblique series together with the transversus remain more or less undifferentiated, but anteriorly, in the chest region, the external oblique muscle gives rise to an *intercostal* series connecting adjacent ribs.

Aves. Among the birds the hypaxial masses are reduced, primarily by the reduction of the oblique and transversus series.

Mammalia. The mammals for the most part resemble the reptiles so far as the epaxial and hypaxial musculature is concerned.

Limb Musculature. The comparative anatomy of the limb musculature is complex and it is difficult to trace true homologies. Current evidence indicates that the limb musculature is not usually formed by a simple budding off from myotomes, but instead is formed from mesenchyme which migrates into the developing limb buds. In the cartilaginous fishes, myotomal buds which develop from the myotomes at the regions where the pectoral and pelvic fins are to be established do give rise to the fin muscles. So far as we know, however, the limb musculature of the higher vertebrates is derived from mesenchyme.

Nevertheless, since the dorsal rami of spinal nerves have always been found to be associated with epaxial muscle masses and the ventral rami with hypaxial muscle masses, and since all of the limb muscles of the vertebrates are invariably innervated by branches of ventral rami, it is assumed that the entire vertebrate limb musculature is derived from the hypaxial muscle masses.

From the point of view of evolution, we may distinguish two sets of limb muscles: *extrinsic* and *intrinsic*.

Extrinsic Muscles. Extrinsic limb muscles extend from the axial skeleton, or from some connective tissue associated with the main portion of the trunk, to the limb skeleton. In other words, extrinsic muscles are those that both hold the limb to the body and move the limb in relation to the body. In general, the extrinsic musculature is relatively more prominent in the primitive vertebrates. Thus, among the fishes, it is the extrinsic muscles that are most in evidence. They form the prominent *levators* and *depressors* that raise and lower the fins, and the *abductors* and *adductors* that erect the fins or bring them next to the body. These extrinsic muscles move the fin as a unit. In the evolution of the tetrapods, the extrinsic muscles of the pectoral appendages are apt to be better developed than those of the pelvic appendages for the simple reason that the pelvic girdle articulates with the axial skeleton, while the pectoral girdle is loosely joined to it by muscles.

Intrinsic Muscles. The intrinsic limb muscles extend from one part of the appendicular skeleton to another and hence move the various parts of the limb in relation to each other. The development of an extensive intrinsic musculature allows for a wide variety of movements. The muscles no longer function as simple levators or depressors, but instead become specialized into *pronators, supinators, extensors, flexors, rotators,* etc.

Special Myotomal Groups. There are in the vertebrate body several sets of muscles that are myotomal in origin but they are not included either with trunk musculature or with limb musculature. The following are four of these groups: (1) extrinsic eye muscles; (2) hypobranchial muscles; (3) dermal muscles; and (4) electric organs.

Extrinsic Eye Muscles. The extrinsic eye muscles are all derived from the myotomes of three small somites that develop in front of the region of the ear (*pro-otic somites*). These are the *pre-*

mandibular somite, the *mandibular* somite, and the *hyoid* somite. The myotome of the premandibular somite gives rise to four eye muscles: the *superior rectus,* the *inferior rectus,* the *internal rectus,* and the *inferior oblique.* Because they come from a single myotome, these muscles are innervated by a single motor nerve, the third cranial, or *oculomotor,* nerve. The myotome of the mandibular somite gives rise to a single eye muscle, the *superior oblique,* which is innervated by the fourth cranial, or *trochlear,* nerve. Finally, the myotome of the third or hyoid somite gives rise to the remaining eye muscle, the *external rectus,* which is innervated by the sixth cranial, or *abducens,* nerve. (In the lamprey, the inferior rectus muscle appears to be innervated by the abducens rather than by the oculomotor nerve. However, the two nerves leave the brain close together and fibers of the third nerve become associated with the sixth. It is these fibers that go to the inferior rectus.)

Hypobranchial Muscles. The muscles under the throat region are myotomal in origin; however, since in this part of the body the development of the branchial apparatus prevents the myotomes from growing downward and around to the throat region, these muscles have to migrate from elsewhere. They develop in the hypaxial masses posterior to the pharynx and migrate ventrally and anteriorly upward under the pharyngeal region. They first appear in the cyclostomes, but in these they are not well differentiated. In the fishes they give rise to such muscles as the *coracoarcuales,* the *coracohyoids,* and the *coracomandibulars.* In the tetrapods, the hypobranchials further differentiate into the *hyoid* and *thyroid* muscles. The *rectus cervicis,* which arises as a forward extension of the rectus abdominis, gives rise to such muscles as the *sternohyoid, sternothyroid, thyrohyoid, geniohyoid,* and *omohyoid.* The tongue musculature of the tetrapods that have well developed tongues is invariably derived from hypobranchial muscles. It includes such muscles as the *genioglossus, hyoglossus, styloglossus,* and the *lingualis* of the mammals.

Dermal Muscles. Voluntary muscles associated with the integument in the vertebrates fall into two general groups depending upon their embryonic origin. The first of these is the *panniculus carnosus* group, which is derived from myotomal musculature. The second is the *sphincter colli* group, which is derived from the branchial group of hypomeric muscles (see p. 81). With few exceptions, myotomal integumentary muscles occur only in the amniotes. (Integumentary muscles are present in the amphibians in the region of the nares where they help control the opening and closing of the external nares.)

The dermal musculature is of some importance to the amniotes. Movements of the scales of a snake are controlled by dermal muscles. In the birds the contraction of the skin muscles brings about the movement of the individual feathers which can thus be ruffled or made to lie prone. The bird can thereby regulate heat radiation to some extent. It is in the mammals that the myotomal integumentary muscles reach their highest development. The twitching movements of the skin that we see in a horse or a cow are controlled by such muscles.

Electric Organs. The electric organs of such fishes as the electric eel, *Electrophorus* (*Gymnotus*), and the star gazer, *Astroscopus,* are derived from myotomal muscle masses. Structurally, these organs consist of a number of layers of tissue put together in a manner resembling the alternation of plates in a storage battery. Although the organs may be distributed in different parts of the body in different species, they are all derived from myotomal muscular tissue. In other fishes, electric organs may be derived from hypomeric muscles or from epidermal structures.

EVOLUTION OF HYPOMERIC MUSCLES

The hypomeric muscles may be divided into two rather distinct groups: the *visceral* muscles, which are involuntary and are associated with visceral organs; and the *branchial* muscles, which become striated and voluntary and are associated with the splanchnocranium and its derivatives.

Visceral Muscles. There are two types of visceral muscles in vertebrates: the smooth, involuntary muscles associated with the viscera and blood vessels; and the cardiac, or heart, muscles, which become striated but remain involuntary in action. Since visceral muscles do not exist as discrete structures, but as parts of organs discussed under other systems (e. g., digestive, circulatory) they will not be considered further here.

Branchial Muscles. The hypomeric muscles associated with the branchial apparatus can be differentiated into four functional groups: the *mandibular arch* group, the *hyoid arch* group, the *glossopharyngeal* group, and the *vagal* group.

Mandibular Group. These are the muscles of mastication in all vertebrates that have jaws. They differentiate into such muscles as the *temporalis* and *masseter,* which close the mouth, and the anterior portion of the *digastric,* which opens the mouth. These muscles are all innvervated by a branch of the fifth cranial (*trigeminal*) nerve.

Hyoid Arch Group. The hyoid arch group in the higher vertebrates comprises such muscles as the *stylohyoid* and the posterior portion of the *digastric*. This group likewise gives rise to a second group of integumentary muscles, the *mimetic* muscles, which are all derived from the sphincter colli mentioned above. These are the muscles that control facial expression. In the turtles and birds, this mass of integumentary muscles simply envelops the neck. The mimetic muscles of most of the lower mammals are rather poorly developed and as a result these animals lack true facial expressions. They are better developed among the carnivores, but it is only in the primates that they are capable of reflecting emotion to any high degree.

All muscles of the hyoid arch group are innervated by branches of the seventh cranial (*facial*) nerve.

Glossopharyngeal Group. The muscles of the glossopharyngeal group serve the first functional gill arch (the third visceral arch) in the elasmobranchs and contribute to the pharyngeal musculature of the third visceral arch in the higher vertebrates. They are innervated by the ninth cranial (*glossopharyngeal*) nerve.

Vagal Group. These muscles serve as the functional muscles controlling the last four gill arches of the elasmobranchs and of all the other groups in which functional gill arches are present. In the higher vertebrates they serve as pharyngeal muscles. In the anamniotes this muscle mass is innervated entirely by the tenth cranial (*vagus*) nerve, but in the amniotes the eleventh cranial (*spinal accessory*) nerve joins with the vagus to innervate this group of muscles.

8

Digestive System

The digestive system consists essentially of a tube, the *alimentary tract,* which passes through the body of the animal from the mouth at one end to the anus or vent at the other, and two associated organs, the liver and the pancreas. The system's function is to prepare the food ingested through the mouth for absorption by the body. Digestion is a chemical process by which complex organic molecules in the food are broken down into simpler ones by the action of enzymes secreted by glands in the walls of the tract and also by the pancreas and liver. These simpler molecules then enter the blood stream through the walls of the tract. Undigested food is eliminated from the body through the anus.

The structure of the digestive system may be modified by three major changes during the evolution of the vertebrate groups. These are: (1) a change in size; (2) a change in diet; and (3) a change from an aquatic to a terrestrial existence.

As an animal increases in size, its volume increases by three dimensions, though its surface increases only by two dimensions; hence, the larger an animal becomes, the greater difference there is between the surface area and the volume of the individual. Since the lining of the digestive system is simply an internal surface, the larger an animal is, the smaller proportionately will its digestive surface be if this does not increase correspondingly in area.

With an increase in size of the vertebrates, there is, in general, a proportional increase in surface of the lining of the digestive tract. This surface may be augmented in four ways: (1) by an increase in diameter; (2) by an increase in length; (3) by an increase in folding; and (4) by the development of supplementary diverticula. Very few organisms have increased the digestive surface by increasing the diameter of the gut; the most common method is to increase its length. Thus, a larger animal tends to have a longer and more extensively coiled gut than does a smaller one. Internal folds of various sorts have developed, including such structures as the *spiral valve*, the *typhlosole*, and the *circular folds* (*plicae circulares*) on the inner surface of the human gut. Supplementary diverticula are present in some animals—for example, the *pyloric caeca* of many of the fishes and the *colic caeca* found in most reptiles, birds, and mammals.

The vast majority of vertebrates are either carnivores or herbivores. Plant food needs to be more thoroughly chewed than does animal food and also takes longer to digest. Herbivorous animals develop effective grinding mechanisms, such as the ridged grinding teeth of many mammals and the muscular gizzards of birds. An increase in the length of time the food remains in the digestive tract is largely accomplished by increasing the length of the gut. This adaptation is strikingly shown by the frogs, in which the intestine of the herbivorous tadpole is long and very coiled, while the intestine of the carnivorous adult is shorter and straighter.

As mentioned above, major evolutionary changes in the vertebrate digestive system result from the transition from aquatic to terrestrial existence. Problems of gathering and digesting food out of water are quite different from problems in the water; a number of changes in the digestive system, such as the development of oral glands and a definitive tongue, are correlated with this major evolutionary step.

DEVELOPMENT OF THE DIGESTIVE SYSTEM

The digestive system develops essentially the same way in all vertebrates.

Embryonic Divisions. The digestive system is formed from three fundamental parts: the stomodaeum, the mesodaeum, and the proctodaeum.

Stomodaeum. The stomodaeum, an invagination at the anterior end of the embryo, is at first separated from the mesodaeum by the *oral plate*. It is lined with ectodermal epithelium.

Mesodaeum. The greater part of the gut is endodermal in origin and is lined with endodermal epithelium.

Proctodaeum. The proctodaeum, an invagination at the posterior end of the embryo, is at first separated from the mesodaeum by the *anal plate.* Like the stomodaeum, it is lined with ectodermal epithelium.

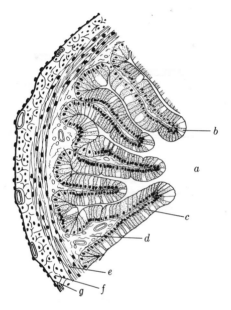

FIG. 8-1. Section through the wall of the stomach: *a,* lumen; *b,* surface epithelium; *c,* lamina propria and muscularis mucosae; *d,* submucosa; *e,* circular layer of smooth muscle fibers; *f,* longitudinal layer of smooth muscle fibers; *g,* visceral peritoneum.

Formation of the Enteron. As the embryo develops, the oral and anal plates rupture so that the mesodaeum becomes continuous with the stomodaeum and proctodaeum. When this occurs, the original primitive gut (*archenteron*) becomes a true tube gut (*enteron*). In the adult there is no sharp line of distinction between stomodaeum, proctodaeum, and mesodaeum. In general, the stomodaeal region ends just posterior to the teeth (when these are present) and the proctodaeal region extends inward to the point where the urogenital tubes join the cloaca in those animals that have a cloaca.

GENERAL STRUCTURE

The digestive tube, or gut, of all vertebrates is complete, extending from the mouth at one end to the anus or vent at the other. It is lined throughout with epithelium. The wall, where it is complete, consists of a number of layers, as follows: (1) an innermost layer of surface epithelium that lines the cavity or *lumen*. This layer rests upon (2) a thin connective tissue layer, the *lamina propria*. Surrounding this is (3) a thin smooth muscle layer, the *muscularis mucosae*. Next there lies (4) a loose meshwork of tissue, the *submucosa*, made up of connective tissue, blood vessels, lymphatic vessels, nervous tissue, etc. The submucosa is surrounded by (5 and 6) smooth muscles arranged in two layers: the inner one comprised of circular muscle fibers, and the outer one of longitudinal muscle fibers. Finally, (7) an outermost *visceral peritoneum* comprises the outer layer of the gut. This outer layer is present only where the gut lies within the coelom. (See Fig. 8-1, p. 85.)

COMPARATIVE ANATOMY OF STOMODAEAL DERIVATIVES

The mouth lining and the structures derived from it develop from the stomodaeum.

Mouth Region. Mouths of vertebrates differ chiefly in the structure of the lips and the development of the oral glands. (For teeth, see p. 65.)

Agnatha. A *buccal funnel* bordered by small *papillae* forms the anterior end of the gut of the cyclostomes. In the lampreys the funnel is lined with numerous horny epidermal teeth which are not homologous with the true teeth of higher vertebrates. No true lips are present to close the mouth, which is permanently open. A so-called "salivary gland" empties into the mouth; its function is unknown.

Chondrichthyes and Osteichthyes. The jawed fishes have rather soft, fleshy lips to close the mouth. Simple mucus-secreting cells are present in the mouth.

Amphibia. Amphibians have fleshy lips. It is to be expected that the vertebrates that made the transition from aquatic to terrestrial existence would be the first to have well developed oral glands. Mucus secreted by these glands moistens the food and makes it easier to swallow. Secretions from such glands would be of little use to an animal whose mouth is constantly bathed with water. An *intermaxillary gland* opens into the roof of the mouth in all the amphibians except the caecilians. The frogs and toads also have *pharyngeal glands.* The protrusible tongues found in most frogs, toads, and salamanders bear mucous glands.

Reptilia. Lips are present in all the reptiles; in the turtles they are hard and cornified. The reptiles have well developed oral glands, as follows: *palatine, lingual, sublingual* (the poison gland of the Gila monster, *Heloderma,* but not poisonous in other reptiles), and *labial glands* (poisonous in some snakes).

Aves. The birds, like the turtles, have hard, cornified lips. Oral glands are reduced. Anterior and posterior sublingual glands are present, as is an *angle gland* at the corner of the mouth which may be homologous with the labial gland of the reptiles.

Mammalia. Lips and well developed oral glands are present in the mammals. Salivary glands, which are universally well developed, include (1) the *parotid,* which leads to the mouth cavity by means of *Stensen's duct;* (2) the *submaxillary gland,* which empties into the mouth by *Wharton's duct;* and (3) the *sublingual gland,* which is drained by *Bartholin's duct* and the *ducts of Rivinus.* The mole and shrew lack sublingual glands. In addition, *orbital glands* which secrete mucus are present in the family Canidae. The artiodactyls have mucous *molar glands.*

Tongue. While the epithelium covering the tongue is stomodaeal in origin, its muscles are derived from myotomes.

Agnatha. The cyclostome tongue, not homologous with that of other vertebrates, is plunger-like and is used for rasping.

Chondrichthyes and Osteichthyes. In these groups the tongue is said to be *primary*—it is a fold of tissue on the floor of the mouth supported by the visceral arches. It can be raised or lowered slightly, but it is not otherwise movable. The tongue is simply covered with epithelium in the Chondrichthyes, but in the Osteichthyes it may bear teeth.

Amphibia. Three conditions of the tongue are found in the amphibians. Certain frogs have secondarily lost the tongue in

evolution and are said to be *aglossal*. The tongue of some salamanders is primary as it was in the fishes. This is the condition
in *Necturus*, the familiar laboratory animal, for example.

A *definitive tongue* is one that has, in addition to the elements
found in the primary tongue, an expanded, movable portion supplied with intrinsic muscles. Such a tongue is present in many
salamanders and most frogs and toads. While there is some variation, many salamanders have a rather mushroom-shaped tongue,
while the frogs and toads usually have a folded tongue in which
the anterior margin is attached whereas the posterior margin is
free.

Reptilia. The tongues of turtles and crocodilians are not protrusible, although they are rather fleshy. The tongue of the
Squamata is forked and protrusible; it is extremely variable in
shape and is highly functional. Certain lizards depend entirely on
the tongue for the capture of food.

Aves. The tongues of birds differ from those of the other tetrapods in that they lack any intrinsic musculature. It is true that
a woodpecker, for example, can move its tongue, but does so by
moving the hyoid arch to which the tongue is attached, not by
moving the tongue proper.

Mammalia. The mammalian tongue is definitive, fleshy, and,
in all orders except the whales, movable. There is some variation
in the structure and function of the tongue in mammals. For
example, in dogs the tongue is used for heat control; in many of
the ruminants it is prehensile; it is used for lapping fluids by
some mammals; and it is used for articulate speech by man.

COMPARATIVE ANATOMY OF MESODAEAL DERIVATIVES

The greater part of the digestive tract is mesodaeal in origin.
Mesodaeal derivatives include the pharynx, the esophagus, the
stomach, and the intestine.

Pharynx. The mouth empties into the pharynx, the first part of
the digestive tract that develops from the mesodaeum. There is a
great deal of variation in the structure of the pharynx and its
derivatives among the different groups of vertebrates, but most
of these changes are more appropriately discussed under other
systems. (See Chapter 9 on the respiratory system and Chapter 15
on the endocrine system.)

Esophagus. The esophagus is the part of the gut that connects the pharynx with the stomach.

Agnatha. The jawless fishes show diversity in the structure of the esophagus. In the hagfish the esophagus continues posteriorly from the pharynx as a simple, tubelike structure. In the lamprey, however, a specialized condition exists which has no parallel in any of the other vertebrates. Two tubes extend posteriorly from the mouth cavity: a ventral pharynx, which ends blindly and is concerned solely with respiration; and a dorsal esophagus, which is continuous posteriorly with the rest of the gut. This is the only vertebrate in which food does not first pass through the pharynx to get to the esophagus.

Chondrichthyes and Osteichthyes. The esophagus of the fishes is simply a short, more or less straight tube whose junction with the stomach is almost imperceptible. The esophagus has longitudinal folds in its wall to permit distention.

Amphibia. Among the amphibians the esophagus is a short, straight tube that seems to be little more than a constricted portion of the gut. Epithelial cells that line the esophagus of the frog are reported to secrete a proenzyme, *pepsinogen,* which apparently is not activated until it reaches the stomach.

Reptilia. Reptiles show a tendency toward an elongation of the esophagus, correlated, to some extent, with elongation of the body. Longitudinal folds in the esophageal wall permit considerable distention, particularly in the snakes. The marine turtles have many pointed, cornified, backward-pointing papillae on the lining of the esophagus. They seem to function in keeping the plants on which the turtles feed moving down the esophagus.

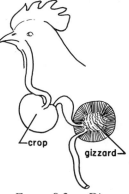

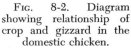

Fig. 8-2. Diagram showing relationship of crop and gizzard in the domestic chicken.

Aves. The esophagus of birds is elongated and has a rather abrupt junction with the stomach. In many birds the esophagus, like that of the sea turtles, is lined with horny papillae. Grain-eating birds and birds of prey have a special pouchlike outgrowth from the ventral wall of the esophagus—the *crop* (see Fig. 8-2). It is here that food is first stored after being swallowed. Apparently the crop has no digestive function, but the food held within it is moistened and the grain seeds tend to swell and soften so that they are more easily digested later on.

A rather peculiar adaptation of pigeons is the development of special crop "glands," which are modified portions of the wall of the crop. They are present in both sexes. Under proper stimulation, these structures (which are not really glands) enlarge. A very rapid cellular proliferation takes place, and a cheesy-looking material called "pigeon milk" is sloughed off into the cavity of the crop. This substance is regurgitated and served to the young squabs as nourishment until they are able to seek their own food. The activity of these crop "glands" is controlled by hormones.

Mammalia. The mammalian esophagus is generally somewhat elongated, and the line of demarcation between it and the stomach is clearly marked. As in other forms, the esophagus bears longitudinal folds to permit expansion.

Stomach. The stomach is basically an enlarged portion of the gut for the temporary storage of food. In most vertebrates it has developed a secondary secretory function through the action of gastric glands which produce digestive enzymes. It is usually separated from the next portion of the gut, the intestine, by a constriction, the *pylorus.*

Agnatha. The cyclostomes lack a true stomach.

Chondrichthyes. The stomach of the elasmobranchs is typically a J-shaped structure with the *pyloric* or posterior portion smaller than the *cardiac* or anterior portion. Chimeras have no stomach.

Osteichthyes. There is some variation in the stomach of the Osteichthyes. In the lungfishes, for example, it is nothing more than a straight, somewhat enlarged tube, lacking any digestive function whatsoever. The stomach of many of the bony fishes is the same as in the Chondrichthyes—a simple, J-shaped structure; however, some of the bony fishes, for example *Polypterus,* have the cardiac and pyloric portions fused along the lines of the lesser curvature, so that the stomach resembles a blind pouch. Many teleosts lack a stomach.

Amphibia. In all of the tetrapods (except the monotremes) the stomach invariably has some digestive function. The shape of the amphibian stomach is often correlated with the shape of the body; in some of the salamanders it is simply a straight tube.

Reptilia. Many reptiles have a long, spindle-shaped stomach in correlation with a long, slender body. Even here, however, there is a rather clear-cut distinction between the stomach and the esophagus. The crocodilians, like the birds, have the wall of the stomach modified into a gizzard-like, muscular structure.

Aves. The avian stomach has become a specialized structure typically divisible into two portions. The expanded _proventriculus_, which is continuous with the esophagus, has a secretory lining which produces digestive juices. Here the food is mixed with the digestive fluid. The food is then passed on to the second portion of the stomach, the much modified and highly muscular _gizzard_. The gizzard represents the posterior or pyloric portion of the stomach. Here the food is ground together with pebbles or grit that the bird has swallowed to aid in breaking up tough material such as the seed coats of grain. The gizzard is best developed in the grain-eating birds and is least developed in the birds of prey and insect-eating forms. In some of these carnivores, little differentiation of the gizzard is noticeable.

Mammalia. The monotremes are unique among the mammals in that they lack epithelial glands in the lining of the stomach, which is thus simply a pouchlike structure for the storage of food.

Other mammals show a great deal of modification in the structure of the stomach. In some mammals, and occasionally in man himself, a constriction may separate the pyloric from the cardiac regions. The stomachs of whales and the aquatic hippopotamus are divided into compartments. The blood-sucking bat, _Desmodus_, has a caecum-like pouch in the pyloric region for the storage of blood when the animal is feeding. In camels, pouchlike diverticula, called _water cells_, arise from the walls of the stomach. They are used for the storage of metabolic water.

The most complex mammalian stomach is that seen in the ruminants, the artiodactyls that chew the cud. The stomach is divided into four separate portions: the _rumen_; the _reticulum_; the _omasum_; and the _abomasum_. Food is swallowed into the rumen, thence passes to the reticulum where it is formed into small balls which are regurgitated, masticated, and reswallowed. The food then passes to the omasum and thence to the abomasum. (See Fig. 8-3, p. 92.)

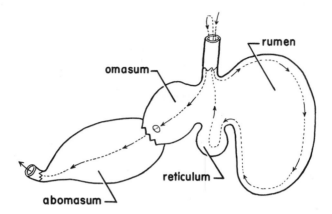

FIG. 8-3. Diagram showing the relationship of parts in, and direction of movement of food through, the ruminant stomach.

Intestine. Most digestion, and all absorption, of food take place in the intestine.

Agnatha. The hagfish and lamprey have a straight intestine. Posteriorly it is slightly enlarged to form a *rectum* which terminates in the *anus*, the opening to the outside. The internal surface of the intestine in the cyclostomes is increased by the presence of a longitudinal fold, the *typhlosole*.

Chondrichthyes. In the cartilaginous fishes the intestine is only slightly folded. It contains a well developed *spiral valve* which functions to increase the internal surface. Some Chondrichthyes have a *cloaca*, a common chamber into which both the digestive tract and the urogenital ducts empty. The external opening of the cloaca is known as the *vent*. Others lack the cloaca and the intestine opens to the outside through the anus.

Osteichthyes. The intestine of the bony fishes is, in general, more folded and looped than that of the cartilaginous fishes. Spiral valves are found in the intestines of the dipnoans and of *Amia* and *Lepisosteus*, and traces of them are present in the intestines of some of the teleosts. However, most teleosts lack such structures.

The small intestine is continuous with the large intestine. In most fishes the posterior part of the large intestine is known as the rectum and opens directly to the outside through the anus. In a few, the large intestine opens into a cloaca.

Many of the fishes have *pyloric caeca* which are diverticula from the intestine just behind the pylorus. These saclike structures increase the surface area of the inner intestinal tract. In some fishes there may be only one caecum, while in other fishes as many as two hundred pyloric caeca may be present.

Amphibia. The caecilian intestine is not differentiated into separate portions, and there is little folding or coiling. More coiling is seen in the salamanders and trachystomes and still more in the frogs and toads. The salamanders and the frogs and toads have a rather sharp division between the small and large intestine, frequently marked by the presence of an *ileocolic valve.* The large intestine opens into a cloaca.

Reptilia. The intestine of the reptiles is similar to that of the frogs. An ileocolic valve lies at the junction of the small and large intestines. In this region, a pouchlike diverticulum of the large intestine, the *colic caecum*, appears for the first time. It is present in all reptiles except the crocodilians and is found in most birds and mammals.

Aves. An increase in the digestive surface area in the birds is brought about by a lengthening of the intestine. The small intestine is long and quite heavily coiled; the large intestine is relatively short and straight, and terminates in a cloaca. One or two colic caeca are present in most birds but are lacking in the parrots, woodpeckers, and some others. The caecum may be large, and in the ostrich it has a spiral fold on its inner surface.

Mammalia. The intestines are more elaborately developed in the mammals than they are in the other vertebrates. The small intestine is divisible into three parts: the *duodenum*, the *jejunum*, and the *ileum*. A pouchlike structure projecting from the lower portion of the ileum to the navel is sometimes present. This structure, known as *Meckel's diverticulum*, represents a portion of the embryonic yolk stalk. An ileocolic valve lies at the junction between the small and large intestines. A colic caecum is present in almost all mammals and may be very large; sometimes two caeca are developed. The distal end of the human caecum has degenerated and is now known as the *vermiform appendix.* In the cony (*Hyrax*) a pair of diverticula develop from the large intestine below the caecum.

COMPARATIVE ANATOMY OF PROCTODAEAL DERIVATIVES

The proctodaeum of the embryo gives rise to the main part of the cloaca and its related structures. Some of these, such as the bladder, will be discussed under the excretory system. There is not much variation in the cloaca when it is present. In some forms, cloacal glands develop from the ectodermal lining of the proctodaeum. Their secretions are used for defense and for sex recognition.

OUTGROWTHS OF THE DIGESTIVE TRACT

In addition to a number of structures derived from the region of the pharynx, two major digestive organs develop as outgrowths of the endodermal wall of the primitive gut.

Liver. The embryonic hepatic diverticulum differentiates into two parts: an anterior *hepatic* portion which develops into the main body of the liver, and a posterior *cystic* portion which gives rise to the gall bladder in which the bile secreted by the liver is stored. Each has its own duct, the *hepatic duct* and the *cystic duct,* respectively. In many animals the hepatic and cystic ducts fuse to form the *common bile duct,* or *ductus choledochus,* which empties into the anterior part of the intestine.

The liver is usually divided into two lobes, right and left, which may be further subdivided. The hagfish has two lobes and two ducts, while the lamprey has only one lobe and duct. The gall bladder is absent in the adult lamprey. In the cartilaginous fishes, bony fishes, amphibians, and reptiles the structure of the liver is rather uniform; in all of them it is large, and in all of them a gall bladder is present. The liver of some birds is quite strongly lobed; many birds lack a gall bladder. There is a good deal of variation in the number of lobes of the mammalian liver—as many as seven may be present. Many mammals lack a gall bladder.

Pancreas. The pancreas is a double-function organ; it serves both as a gland of internal secretion (see endocrine system) and as a digestive gland. The digestive juices secreted by the pancreas contain a number of enzymes (*trypsin, maltase,* etc.). These secretions usually enter the intestine by means of a dorsal duct, the *duct of Santorini,* and a ventral duct, the *duct of Wirsung.* These ducts sometimes fuse with the ductus choledochus.

In the cyclostomes the pancreas apparently functions only as an endocrine organ. Among the cartilaginous and bony fishes it may vary from a quite diffuse structure primarily endocrine in nature, to a rather well defined organ. The pancreas does not differ greatly among the amphibians, reptiles, birds, and mammals. One duct or several may be present. They may enter the intestine separately or join the ductus choledochus. The cat sometimes has a *pancreatic bladder* in which digestive secretions of the pancreas are temporarily stored.

9

Respiratory System

The respiratory system has the function of bringing about an exchange of oxygen and carbon dioxide between the organism and the environment in which it lives. In the vertebrates, there is one major trend in the evolution of this system that is readily apparent, namely, the modifications brought about with the change from the aquatic, pisciform vertebrates (for which water is the surrounding medium) to the terrestrial tetrapods (for which air is the surrounding medium). As we shall see, this shift of environment has brought about a number of modifications in the respiratory system; the predominant one is the change from gill respiration to lung respiration.

PHARYNGEAL POUCHES

Since the structure of the respiratory system of the vertebrates is closely associated with the structure of the pharynx, we shall begin by reviewing briefly the evolution of the pharynx and its pouches.

Formation of Pharyngeal Pouches. In the embryonic development of all vertebrates, a series of evaginated pouches lined with endoderm form in the lateral wall of the pharynx. On the outer wall of the pharynx, exactly opposite these *visceral,* or *pharyngeal, pouches,* are a series of invaginating *visceral furrows* that are lined with ectoderm. The furrows reach inward until they are separated from the pouches only by a thin, platelike layer of endoderm and ectoderm.

The number of pouches is, in general, larger in the more primitive vertebrates and smaller in the higher groups. Among the cyclostomes from six to fourteen pairs may be present. In the Chondrichthyes and Osteichthyes, as well as among the amphibians and reptiles, five or six pairs are commonly found. Four is the usual number of pouches in the endothermal birds and mammals.

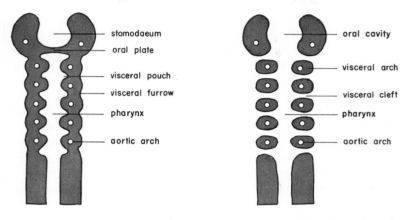

FIG. 9-1. Frontal section through pharyngeal region of hypothetical vertebrate embryo, showing relationship of visceral pouches, visceral furrows, visceral arches, and visceral clefts. Left, before the plates separating the pouches and furrows perforate; right, after the plates have perforated, resulting in the formation of visceral clefts. (Redrawn from Weichert, *Elements of Chordate Anatomy*, McGraw-Hill, 1959, by permission.)

Formation of Visceral Clefts and Visceral Arches. In all the anamniotes, the thin plate between pouch and furrow perforates so that the endoderm lining the pharynx becomes continuous with the ectoderm of the outer surface of the body. A slit known as the *visceral slit* or *visceral cleft* thus develops in the wall of the pharynx. Even in the amniotes temporary perforations may occasionally occur. The visceral pouches are separated by the *visceral arches.* (Fig. 9-1.)

Formation of Gill Arches and Gill Slits. The pisciform vertebrates have respiratory structures known as *gills* associated with the visceral arches. A visceral arch which bears gills is known as a *gill arch* and a visceral slit or cleft which has gills on its walls is known as a *gill slit.*

Evolution of Visceral Slits and Gill Slits. There is some variation in the number of visceral slits and gill slits in the vertebrates.

Pisciform Vertebrates. Sometimes the first visceral slit does not bear a true gill and is smaller in size than the others; it is known as the *spiracle*. Typically in most fishlike vertebrates, four or five clefts follow the spiracle if it is present. Frequently, the spiracle is absent; thus, in most fishes it is not the first visceral pouch but the second that makes the first slit.

Amphibia. Among the amphibians, five pairs of pharyngeal pouches form in the usual manner during embryonic development. The first develops into the Eustachian tube and middle ear. The second, third, and fourth perforate, but the fifth usually does not form more than a pouch and rarely perforates. In most amphibians all of the perforated gill slits close over at metamorphosis, but in some of the salamanders and in all of the trachystomes one or more remain open. Such forms as *Necturus* have two pairs of gill clefts in the adult stage; the Hellbender, *Cryptobranchus*, has only one pair. The trachystome, *Siren,* has three clefts remaining open.

Amniota. In all of the amniotes, the first pharyngeal pouch becomes the Eustachian tube and middle ear, but the other pouches are reduced and do not typically rupture through to the outside. Five pairs of pouches are formed in the reptiles, only four in the birds and mammals.

GILLS

The typical vertebrate gill is composed of numerous *gill filaments* which are simply thin-walled extensions of epithelial surfaces. These filaments are richly endowed with blood vessels, thus providing a mechanism to facilitate the exchange of gases between the blood and the environment.

Types of Gills. In general, two types of gills are recognized— external and internal.

External Gills. External gills are usually formed by a simple branching of the epithelial ectoderm on the outer surfaces of the visceral arches. They are typically larval structures which do not persist in the adult.

Internal Gills. Internal gills are usually composed of series of *lamellae* which are borne on the anterior and posterior faces of the visceral arches. The series of internal gill filaments on the wall of a gill arch is termed a *hemibranch* (*demibranch*), while two hemibranchs which enclose between them a gill arch make up an entire gill, or *holobranch*. Like the external gills, they are apparently ectodermal in origin.

Comparative Anatomy of Gills. Since gills are organs for respiration in an aquatic medium, they are found only in the fishlike vertebrates, larval amphibians, and a few aquatic adult amphibians.

Agnatha. The lamprey has seven pairs of gill slits, each of which bears a hemibranch on its anterior and one on its posterior wall. Thus, there are fourteen hemibranchs on each side in the adult lamprey. Each gill slit opens individually to the outside. The hagfish has six pairs of gill slits. These slits do not open individually to the outside, but instead continue as long tubes which ultimately unite to form a common duct on each side leading to the outside by a single opening.

Chondrichthyes and Osteichthyes. In the Chondrichthyes the gill arch (*interbranchial septum*) between two hemibranchs is extremely well developed and extends to the outside so that the gill slits open to the outside by a series of separate openings.

The interbranchial septa of the bony fishes are reduced and the entire complement of gills is covered by a bony *operculum*. Thus, there is but a single opening to the outside, instead of a series of openings as in the cartilaginous fishes. The bony fishes have typically five well developed visceral slits, although these may not all bear hemibranchs and thus may not all be true gill slits. The larvae of dipnoans and of *Polypterus* have external gills.

Amphibia. The gill slits of tadpoles, which are, of course, the larval stages of frogs and toads, develop in the same manner as do those of the fishes; however, the gills of these animals are always external gills that develop from the outer margins of the visceral arches. In the tadpole the first pouch fails to perforate and forms the Eustachian tube and middle ear cavity. Pouch five is usually transitory and seldom perforates to become a slit; only pouches two, three, and four rupture to the exterior, and it is these that form the transient gill slits of the tadpole. The external gills of the tadpole are at first exposed to the outer world, but a fold of skin called an *operculum* (it is not bony as in the bony fishes) soon grows back to cover them over. The cavities contained by the right and left opercular structures become confluent ventrally and the right one usually closes, leaving only a small cleft on the left side for the expulsion of water. This opening is known as a *spiracle,* but it is in no sense homologous with the spiracle of the dogfish which is a true visceral cleft.

The salamanders and caecilians also typically pass through larval stages in which they exhibit gill slits and external gills. Usually at metamorphosis the external gills wither and disappear and the gill slits close so that the adult has no trace remaining of the gills or gill slits. Some salamanders, though, and all of the trachystomes retain gill slits and functional gills as adults.

The retention of the larval body form, including functional gills, by sexually mature amphibians may be the result either of environmental or of hereditary factors. When it is caused by some factor in the environment, such as a lack of iodine, which results in a malfunctioning of the thyroid gland and a consequent failure of the animal to metamorphose, the situation is properly called *neoteny.* Neotenic salamanders can be made to metamorphose by the administration of the proper hormones or minerals. In other animals such as *Necturus,* failure to metamorphose is not under environmental control but is due to heredity. These animals cannot be made to lose the gills. Genetically fixed failure to metamorphose is known as *paedogenesis.*

Reptilia, Aves, Mammalia. None of the reptiles, birds, or mammals have gills of any sort.

SWIM BLADDERS AND LUNGS

It is the consensus among comparative anatomists and paleontologists that the swim bladders of the modern fishes and the lungs of the tetrapods had a common origin in some lunglike structure of the early primitive placoderms. Nevertheless, it is convenient to discuss them as two separate units; hence, we will look first at the comparative anatomy of the swim bladder and then at the comparative anatomy of the tetrapod lung and its accompanying air ducts.

Comparative Anatomy of Swim Bladder. The swim bladder is a gas-filled sac which arises as a diverticulum from the anterior part of the digestive tract. It is significant that only in some of the lower fishes and the dipnoans does the swim bladder function in any way as an aid to respiration. The swim bladder of the higher fishes serves primarily either as a simple, hydrostatic organ (or occasionally as an organ for sound production and reception) or has disappeared entirely.

Chondrichthyes. None of the adult Chondrichthyes has a swim bladder; however, in several species a rudiment shows up during early embryonic development.

Osteichthyes. In the bony fishes many different situations occur; some fishes have no swim bladder at all. In most teleosts a swim bladder is present but is not connected with the digestive tract by means of a duct; it is simply an isolated sac lying dorsal to the digestive tract and depending upon the circulatory system to add or take gas from it. This type of swim bladder is termed *physoclistous,* whereas the type that retains a duct (*pneumatic duct*) leading to the outside by way of the digestive tract is termed *physostomous.*

Physostomous swim bladders show much variation. Usually the duct opens from the dorsal surface of the digestive tract and the bladder lies above the gut. The bladder may or may not be bilobed. The dorsal, bilobed swim bladder of both the bowfin, *Amia,* and the garfish, *Lepisosteus,* is endowed with a rich supply of capillaries and functions as a lung of sorts. A similar structure is seen in the lungfish, *Neoceratodus,* but here the duct comes from the ventral side of the gut and passes around it to the dorsal swim bladder. The swim bladder of the primitive chondrostean, *Polypterus,* is a ventral, bilobed sac which may function as a lung. The other dipnoans resemble *Polypterus* in having a ventral, bilobed sac with the duct on the ventral side of the gut. In the lungfishes the swim bladder is vasculated and serves as a lung for respiration.

Tetrapod Air Ducts and Lungs. While none of the tetrapods has a true swim bladder, the bilobed diverticulum from the ventral portion of the pharynx which gives rise to the lungs seems to be logically derived from some such swim bladder as the ventrally located, bilobed, vasculated swim bladder found, for example, in the dipnoan *Protopterus.* (Note, however, that it must not be assumed for this reason that the amphibians evolved from the lungfishes; they almost certainly did not.)

The *lung buds* of the tetrapods typically form on the floor of the pharynx posterior to the pharyngeal pouches, although it has been reported that in some of the amphibians the last two pharyngeal pouches give rise to the lung buds. Growing downward and posteriorly, the lung buds become invested with mesoderm to form the adult lung. The degree of branching and of vascularization of the lung varies with the species.

The *trachea* is the unpaired duct that connects the lungs with the floor of the pharynx. The anterior end of the trachea of many tetrapods is modified into a *larynx,* or *voice box,* which opens into the pharynx by means of the slitlike *glottis.* The walls of the trachea, larynx, and glottis are supported by cartilages.

Comparative Anatomy of Larynx. The walls of the larynx are supported by visceral cartilages which, with the loss of gills, have become modified to support the median voice box. Support of the air duct at this place by visceral cartilages is unknown in fishes, in which these cartilages still retain their original function.

AMPHIBIA. The common laboratory amphibian, *Necturus,* has about the simplest kind of larynx found among the amphibians. The larynx is supported by a pair of *lateral cartilages* derived from the last pair of visceral arches. The more specialized amphibians show further modifications in that this pair of lateral cartilages is supplemented by *arytenoid* and *cricoid cartilages.* The salamanders of the family Plethodontidae, in which pulmonary respiration has been lost, lack lungs, trachea, and larynx.

Most of the caudate amphibians have poorly developed voices, if any. *Vocal cords* composed of elastic fibers are present in the larynx of the salientians, particularly the male frogs. Furthermore, male frogs develop large diverticula from the mouth cavity known as *vocal sacs,* which act as resonators. Frogs call out by passing air from the lungs to the vocal sacs and back again across the vocal cords while keeping the mouth and nostrils closed.

REPTILIA. All reptiles except the crocodilians have the larynx in about the same stage of development as it is in the amphibians. Most reptiles lack well developed vocal cords, but they are present in the larynx of some of the lizards (geckos and a few others) which have distinct, guttural voices. In addition to the cartilages already mentioned, a *thyroid cartilage* is present in the crocodilian larynx. Male crocodilians make bellowing noises that can be heard for a distance of several miles.

AVES. Somewhat surprisingly, perhaps, the larynx of birds is not fully developed and is incapable of producing sound. A unique structure, the *syrinx,* is the organ responsible for the bird's voice.

MAMMALIA. It is in the mammals that the larynx becomes most complicated. In addition to arytenoid and cricoid cartilages, the mammals have a well developed *thyroid cartilage,* heretofore seen only in the crocodilians. A cartilaginous flap, the *epiglottis,* guards the opening of the glottis.

Most mammals have two sets of cords, known as *false vocal cords* and *true vocal cords.* The true vocal cords divide the larynx into two portions, of which the anterior is known as the *vestibule.* The false vocal cords extend into the vestibule from either side for a short distance. Both types of cords are not found in all species of mammals. Elephants, for example, lack false vocal cords, while the hippopotamus lacks true vocal cords. It is said that the purring of a cat is produced by the false vocal cords.

Comparative Anatomy of Trachea and Bronchi. The trachea is the main pipeline leading from the larynx to the lungs. At its posterior end it usually divides into paired bronchi.

AMPHIBIA. Among the caudate amphibians the trachea is generally rather short, but in some of the elongated, aquatic forms, such as *Amphiuma,* and in the trachystomes it is quite elongated. The trachea of the caecilians is moderate in length and is supported by cartilages which form half rings as contrasted with the small and irregular cartilages in the caudate amphibians. The trachea is so short in most frogs and toads that it can hardly be said to exist, but in the tropical Pipidae, in which the lungs function as hydrostatic organs, a definite trachea can be found. In all of the amphibians the trachea divides at its posterior end into two bronchi.

REPTILIA. Among the reptiles the development of the trachea is rather closely correlated with the elongation of the body. It tends to be shortest in the lizards and more elongated in the crocodilians and snakes. Turtles, which have relatively long necks, also have long tracheas. In *Sphenodon,* lizards, and a number of snakes some of the cartilages form complete rings around the trachea. Although the trachea of most reptiles leads into a pair of bronchi, some snakes have only one bronchus (right) which leads to the single lung.

AVES. The trachea of a bird is usually extremely well developed and may even exceed the neck in length. The swan trachea, for example, forms a loop which rests in a cavity of the breastbone. The tracheal cartilages of the birds usually form complete rings.

The trachea leads into paired bronchi. The penguins have a unique specialization in that a median partition divides the trachea into a pair of tubes. As was mentioned earlier, the larynx of birds is not the voice-producing organ; the syrinx is the true organ of sound production. This resonance chamber may comprise only the enlarged posterior end of the trachea, or it may also include the expanded anterior ends of the two bronchi, or it may be formed entirely from the anterior bronchi.

MAMMALIA. The length of the trachea in mammals is correlated with the development of the neck. It is relatively short in the aquatic cetaceans and sirenians, and, of course, is extremely elongated in such creatures as the long-necked giraffe. The tracheal cartilages are usually incomplete on the dorsal side. The trachea typically divides into two bronchi, but a few mammals have an extra bronchus on the right side.

Comparative Anatomy of Lungs. The evolution of the tetrapod lung involved an increase in both the area and the efficiency of the respiratory surface together with an adaptation to the shape of the body.

AMPHIBIA. In general, the lungs of amphibians are rather simple. The left lung of the Apoda is vestigial, and the larger right one is the functional lung. In most other amphibians the left lung is usually larger. Caudate lungs vary widely, ranging from the condition seen in *Necturus,* in which the lungs are two simple sacs, to that in some salamanders in which the proximal half of each lung is considerably modified by an elaboration of folds in its wall.

As we have noted (p. 102), salamanders of the family Plethodontidae lack lungs entirely. They respire solely through the skin and the mucous membrane lining the mouth and pharynx. As would be expected, the lungs of frogs and toads are shorter and more spherical in shape than are those of the more elongated salamanders. The inner wall of the frog's lung is somewhat modified and divided into little stall-like compartments, thus increasing appreciably the respiratory surface of the lung.

REPTILIA. Further modification increasing the respiratory surface is seen in the reptiles. The lung of *Sphenodon* is formed somewhat like a group of frog lungs closely tied together. In most snakes the left lung usually is greatly reduced or absent, while the large right one is the functional lung, but among the more primitive boas and their relatives both lungs are present,

the left simply being somewhat shorter than the right. Some lizards have pouchlike diverticula from the walls of the lungs which
increase their surface. The crocodilian lung is further modified
into pouchlike cavities and resembles the mammalian lung described below.

Aves. Bird lungs are unique. The bronchus passes through the
lung and gives rise to smaller *parabronchi,* which in turn give
rise to tiny, capillary-like vessels, *air capillaries.* These rejoin the
parabronchi or the main bronchus. The end of the bronchus divides into smaller branches leading into *air sacs* which are distributed widely through the trunk of the bird and may even enter
cavities in the bones. These air sacs presumably permit a sort of
forced ventilation of the lungs with each breath of these highly
active vertebrates.

Mammalia. In the mammalian lungs the bronchi divide and re-
divide into smaller and smaller ducts, *bronchioles,* which ultimately terminate in pockets called *alveoli.* These alveoli are
supplied with a rich capillary network, and it is here that the
gaseous exchange takes place. The lungs of mammals are usually
divided into two or more lobes, and there is generally an asym-
metry between the lungs in this respect. Thus, man has three
lobes in the right lung but only two in the left. Some mammals,
such as the elephants and their allies and the perissodactyls, resemble the other groups of tetrapods in that their lungs are not
divided into lobes. The right lung of the egg-laying mammals is
divided into lobes, but the left is not.

COMPARATIVE ANATOMY OF NASAL PASSAGES

In the air-breathing vertebrates there is a very close relationship between the olfactory organs and the respiratory structures.
This is obviously a practical arrangement because the air containing the volatile substances that stimulate the olfactory organs
is precisely the same air that is used in respiration. Hence, the
nares, which started out as simple olfactory organs, became
closely associated with the respiratory system during the course
of evolution. (The nares as olfactory organs will be discussed in
Chap. 14.)

Chondrichthyes. None of the Chondrichthyes has a closed nasal
passage from the external nostril (naris) to the mouth, but a
probable forerunner of such a passage may be seen in the *oronasal*

groove which runs from the naris to the corner of the mouth in some elasmobranchs.

Osteichthyes. A true nasal passage, a direct connection between the nasal and mouth cavities, appears for the first time in the bony fishes of the subclass Choanichthyes. The openings on the front of the face are known as the *external nares;* the openings into the mouth at the other ends of the tubes are known as the *internal nares* or *choanae* (from which the name of this subclass is derived). It is perhaps worth noting that the nasal passage first appears in the group of fishes in which the swim bladder is most similar in function to the tetrapod lung.

Amphibia. All the amphibians have complete nasal passages, though they are short and rather simple. In the aquatic stages and in the neotenic and paedogenic forms, water instead of air passes through the nasal passages. Many aquatic amphibians have valves around the internal nares to control the direction of the flow of water. Some salamanders have projections from the lateral walls into the nasal passages, the first indication of the conchae which later become so highly developed in some of the mammals.

Reptilia. The reptiles show an appreciable elongation of the nasal passages through the development of a *secondary palate—* a hard, bony structure that divides the mouth cavity into a dorsal *nasal portion* and a ventral *oral portion.* The secondary palate is formed from shelflike projections of the premaxillary, palatine, and pterygoid bones. These projections are only partially developed in most reptiles, but in the crocodilians the bones fuse at the midline to form a complete plate. As a result, the internal openings of the nasal passages are located rather far down the throat. Most reptiles have a single, quite simple concha projecting from the lateral wall of the nasal passage, but crocodilians have three conchae.

Aves. The nasal passages of the birds are short because the secondary palate fails to fuse along the median line, giving rise to what is known as a *cleft palate.* Three conchae extend into the nasal passages. Only one of them has olfactory receptors in its epithelium. The conchae are covered with a glandular mucous membrane whose secretions aid in warming and moistening the air as it passes through the nasal passages on its way to the lungs.

Mammalia. The nasal passages of mammals are highly developed and are strikingly more elongated than they are in the lower forms. All the mammals have a well developed secondary *hard palate* formed from the premaxillary and palatine bones. In addition, a posteriorly extending *soft palate* composed of connective tissue carries the nasal passages farther posteriorly so that the choanae actually open into the pharyngeal region. Anterior elongation of the nasal passages is produced by the *nose.* In a few mammals the nose is excessively developed and forms a *proboscis* with the external nares located at its tip.

The elongated nasal passage of the mammal is differentiated into three regions—the *vestibular,* the *respiratory,* and the *olfactory.* The vestibule is the most anterior; it is lined with skin which extends from the outside and becomes continuous with the inner mucous membrane. Hairs and sebaceous glands are often abundant in the vestibule. Posterior to the vestibule are the respiratory and olfactory regions which make up the greater part of the nasal cavity. Projecting into these regions are a series of exceedingly well developed, scroll-like conchae or *turbinate bones.* They project from the nasal, maxillary, and ethmoid bones and are known as *nasoturbinates, maxilloturbinates,* and *ethmoturbinates,* respectively. The nasoturbinates and maxilloturbinates are covered with respiratory epithelium which is ciliated and rich in secretory cells. The olfactory epithelium covers much of the ethmoturbinates; thus, the mammals have an increased sensory area of olfactory epithelium. In man there has been a reduction of the turbinate bones and a corresponding reduction in the sense of smell.

MISCELLANEOUS RESPIRATORY ORGANS

While gills and lungs constitute the main respiratory organs of most vertebrates, in some groups there are other structures that carry on the process of respiration.

The *yolk sac* serves partly as a respiratory structure in the embryos of some elasmobranchs, of the birds, and of certain lower mammals. Another embryonic structure, the *allantois,* serves as a temporary respiratory organ in the amniotes.

The *skin* is a very important respiratory organ in a great many vertebrates. Eels, for example, can survive out of water for many hours and sometimes migrate overland through damp grass, receiving their oxygen through cutaneous respiration. It has already been mentioned that the lungless salamanders of the family Plethodontidae depend very largely on the skin for respiration. One of the African frogs has a growth of filamentous structures on the body surface which give it a hairy appearance (hence the common name "hairy frog") and serve as respiratory surfaces.

Buccopharyngeal respiration (through the lining of the mouth and pharynx) takes place in the lungless salamanders and in the soft-shell turtles. Some aquatic turtles utilize a vascular cloaca as an accessory respiratory organ, and some fishes use a highly vascular rectum for the exchange of gases.

10

Excretory System

The excretory system of the vertebrates is very closely associated with the reproductive system, and both systems together are usually referred to as the urogenital or urinogenital system. Nevertheless, the excretory system has its own specialized structures and functions. Control of the salt and water content and elimination of metabolic waste products are functions of the excretory system. The end products of metabolism include carbon dioxide, ammonia, urea, uric acid, creatine, pigments, and inorganic salts. The elimination of carbon dioxide is accomplished by the respiratory system. With certain exceptions, the other wastes are eliminated by the excretory or urinary organs. Usually these substances are in solution in water, in which case the final product, as eliminated by the body, is known as *urine*.

Except for a few structures near the distal openings of some of the ducts, the entire excretory system is derived from the embryonic mesomere.

FUNCTIONAL UNIT OF KIDNEY

The functional unit of the typical vertebrate kidney is made up of two parts: the *renal,* or *Malpighian, corpuscle,* and the *nephric,* or *uriniferous, tubule.*

Malpighian Corpuscle. The Malpighian corpuscle consists of a *glomerulus* and a *Bowman's capsule.* A glomerulus is a small, rounded mass of capillaries originating from an *afferent arteriole,* a branch of the renal artery. These capillaries reunite to form an *efferent arteriole.* Bowman's capsule is a double-walled, cup-shaped structure which surrounds the glomerulus. The cavity be-

tween the two walls of Bowman's capsule is continuous with that
of the nephric tubule (Fig. 10-1).

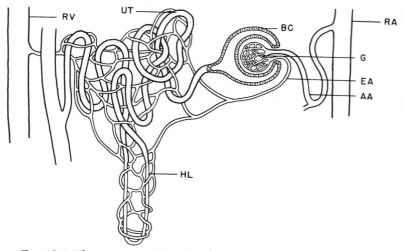

Fig. 10-1. The structure of the Malpighian body in the metanephric kidney. RA, renal artery; BC, Bowman's capsule; G, glomerulus; EA, efferent
arteriole; AA, afferent arteriole; UT, uriniferous tubule; RV, renal vein; HL,
loop of Henle.

Nephric Tubule. At one end, the kidney tubule originates at a
Bowman's capsule, and its walls are continuous with the outer
wall of the capsule. The tubule may be elongated and coiled. At
the other end it opens into a kidney duct.

Function of Malpighian Corpuscle and Tubule. The fluid part
of the blood passes readily through the thin walls of the glomeru-
lar vessels and Bowman's capsule to enter the nephric tubule, but
blood cells and certain large molecules are prevented from filter-
ing through these walls. Thus the fluid in the proximal end of the
tubule is very similar to blood plasma. It is made up mostly of
water and contains, in addition to metabolic waste products, such
substances as sugars and salts that are still useful to the body. As
this fluid passes down the tubule, there is a selective reabsorption
through the wall of the tubule into the surrounding capillaries so
that much water and the useful substances are returned to the
blood. As a result, the urine that is finally voided differs greatly
in composition from blood plasma. In particular, urine contains a
much higher concentration of urea or uric acid.

TYPES OF KIDNEYS

During the evolution of the vertebrates, a series of kidney types replaced each other as the functional excretory organs.

Archinephros. It seems probable that the excretory organ of the primitive, ancestral vertebrate was of a type that has been named the *archinephros*.

Structure of Archinephros. This primitive kidney is thought to have consisted of a series of *archinephric tubules,* one tubule on each side of each body segment. Each of these tubules opened into the coelom by a ciliated, funnel-shaped opening called a *nephrostome*. Glomeruli were suspended segmentally in the coelomic cavity adjacent to the nephrostomes. Fluids eliminated by the glomeruli were collected by the nephrostomes and passed down the archinephric tubules.

The tubules emptied into a pair of *archinephric ducts,* one on each side of the dorsal wall of the body cavity. These ducts extended for the whole length of the body cavity.

Distribution of Archinephros. No adult, living vertebrate possesses an archinephros, but it is present in the larval form of the hagfish (*Myxine*) and the larvae of some of the caecilians (Apoda).

Pronephros. The most primitive type of kidney functional in an adult vertebrate is the *pronephros.*

Structure of Pronephros. The pronephros is believed to represent the most anterior part of the ancestral archinephros.

Tubules and Malpighian Corpuscles. In the embryos of all vertebrates, the first kidney tubules arise from the anterior end of the mesomere. In a few primitive forms the glomeruli, which are derived from segmental branches of the dorsal aorta, project into the coelom near the nephrostomes. Such structures are known as *external glomeruli.* Usually, however, the glomerulus is *internal* —that is, it is almost completely surrounded by a Bowman's capsule which projects from the tubule near its proximal end. The nephrostome persists and still retains its opening to the coelom. Whether the glomeruli are external or internal seems to have no particular significance.

Because of the segmental nature of the pronephros and the relatively small number of tubes and related structures, the dif-

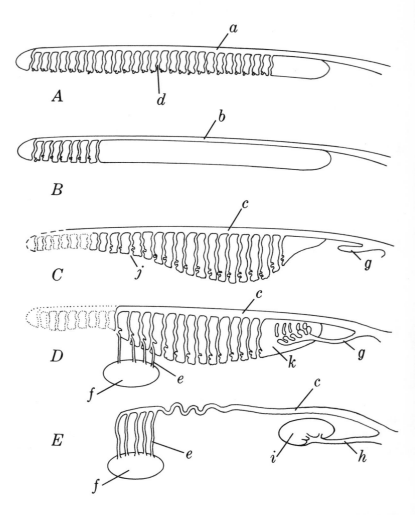

FIG. 10-2. Evolution of vertebrate kidneys and ducts. *A*, archinephros; *B*, pronephros; *C*, mesonephros; *D*, opisthonephros (male); *E*, metanephros (male): *a*, archinephric duct; *b*, pronephric duct; *c*, Wolffian duct; *d*, archinephric tubule; *e*, efferent ductule; *f*, testis; *g*, developing ureter; *h*, ureter; *i*, metanephric kidney; *j*, nephrostome; *k*, metanephric portion of opisthonephros. In females the efferent ductules do not pass to the gonads and the Wolffian ducts become vestigial in forms with metanephric kidneys. (Redrawn from Hyman, *Comparative Vertebrate Anatomy*, 2nd ed., University of Chicago Press, 1942. Copyright 1922 and 1942 by the University of Chicago.)

fuse pronephric kidney does not form a distinct organ identifiable to the naked eye. For example, there are thirteen tubules in the lamprey, seven in the 3 mm. human embryo, and four in the shark embryo.

DUCT OF PRONEPHROS. The pronephric tubules fuse to form the *pronephric* (originally archinephric) *duct* which grows backward and opens posteriorly into the cloaca. While the pronephros may be important to those organisms in which it is functional, its chief evolutionary significance seems to be the part it plays in forming the pronephric duct, which persists after the pronephros itself has disappeared.

Distribution of Pronephros. The pronephric tubules continue to function in the adult hagfish and in occasional teleosts. The pronephros is also a functioning structure in many immature fishes and in the larvae of some of the amphibians and appears transitorily in the embryos of all the higher vertebrates.

Mesonephros and Opisthonephros. The *mesonephros* is the kidney tissue that develops posterior to the pronephros. Posterior to the mesonephros, the *metanephros* (that portion of the kidney tissue that gives rise to the adult amniote kidney) develops. The adult kidney of the anamniotes involves not only the mesonephric tissue but some of the metanephric tissue as well. Thus, while the kidney of the anamniotes is frequently called a mesonephros, it is not completely homologous with the mesonephros of the amniote embryo, and for this reason is preferably referred to as the *opisthonephros.*

Structure of Mesonephros and Opisthonephros. These kidney structures form discrete organs that are readily apparent as kidneys. They resemble each other closely in structure and function.

TUBULES AND MALPIGHIAN CORPUSCLES. While the first few mesonephric tubules tend to be segmentally distributed, proliferation of many such tubules in each of the body segments eventually obliterates all evidence of metamerism. Thus, for the first time in evolution, the primary excretory organ becomes a discrete, bulky structure, lying against the dorsal body wall and tending to bulge into the coelom.

The embryonic tubules are first formed as solid structures, but they soon develop lumina and begin to elongate. One end of the tubule enlarges and is invaginated by the ball of capillaries forming the glomerulus and thus becomes the double-walled Bowman's capsule described above. This capsule, with its included glomerulus, forms the renal or Malpighian corpuscle. All glomeruli in the opisthonephros are surrounded by Bowman's capsules and hence are internal. In a few forms, *peritoneal funnels* (nephrostomes) may connect the tubules with the coelom, but this seems to be the exception. Most species that have been studied have lost the peritoneal funnels and the coelom is no longer continuous with the outside world through the excretory system.

At first, as the mesonephric tubule develops and elongates, it becomes S-shaped, and then the proximal and distal loops of the S fold further to form the typical *proximal* and *distal convolutions* so characteristic of the mesonephric tubule.

MESONEPHRIC DUCT. The distal ends of the tubules establish connections with the old pronephric duct, which is now known as the *mesonephric duct* (also called *Wolffian duct*). The distal ends of several tubules may unite before they join the mesonephric duct, and sometimes the tube formed from the components of several tubules may establish an opening directly into the cloaca rather than into the mesonephric duct. The mesonephric duct may also transport sperm to the outside.

Distribution of Opisthonephros and Mesonephros. The opisthonephros is the functional kidney of the adult lamprey, the cartilaginous fishes, the bony fishes, and the amphibians. The mesonephric part functions in the embryos of reptiles, birds, and mammals.

Metanephros. The metanephric kidney develops from the most posterior portion of the mesomere and is the most compact of any of the vertebrate renal structures.

Structure of the Metanephros. The body of the metanephros has a twofold origin. Part of it develops from the posterior end of the opisthonephros, while another part forms as a new and unique metanephric structure.

MALPIGHIAN CORPUSCLES AND NEPHRIC TUBULES. The metanephric kidney is basically made up of the same structures as the mesonephros—the Malpighian corpuscles and their associated tubules. No nephrostomes (or peritoneal funnels) are ever present in the metanephros. The metanephric tubules are somewhat more complex in the mammals and (to a lesser extent) in the birds than are the mesonephric tubules. In these animals, each tubule develops a long loop (the *loop of Henle*) with ascending and descending portions between the proximal and distal convoluted segments. These loops function primarily in the reabsorption of water.

COLLECTING TUBULES AND METANEPHRIC DUCT. In the amniote embryo, a diverticulum develops near the posterior end of the mesonephric or Wolffian duct and grows outward and forward to make contact with the developing metanephros. This diverticulum branches and rebranches within the metanephros to form a large number of very fine *collecting tubules*. These collecting tubules establish connections with the S-shaped renal tubules, and henceforth the waste products pass through them to the new duct formed from the diverticulum. This duct is called a *ureter*. When this new pathway develops and the embryonic mesonephros degenerates, the Wolffian duct no longer transports urine from the kidney but remains as a reproductive duct transporting sperm from the testis.

Distribution of the Metanephros. The metanephros becomes functional in most reptile, bird, and mammal embryos and is the functional kidney of all adult amniotes.

COMPARATIVE ANATOMY OF KIDNEYS AND RELATED STRUCTURES

The evolutionary history and embryonic development of the kidney types are so closely related that it is better to consider them together (see Table 2).

Agnatha. As was pointed out above (p. 111), the embryo hagfish has a kidney of the archinephric type. In the adult, however, the anterior end is modified to form a persistent *head kidney*, or pronephros. Posterior to this pronephros, an opisthonephric kidney develops which differs but little structurally from the archinephros except that the posterior tubules lose their peritoneal funnels.

The adult lamprey lacks a pronephros. The opisthonephric kidneys form long, strap-shaped structures which lie in the coelom suspended by mesentery-like membranes on either side of the mid-dorsal line. There are no peritoneal funnels in the adult. In *Petromyzon,* at least, a vestige of the old archinephric

TABLE 2

DISTRIBUTION OF THE TYPES OF VERTBRATE KIDNEY

	Pronephros	Opisthonephros or Mesonephros	Metanephros
Agnatha			
Hagfish	Adult	Adult	
Lamprey	Embryo	Adult	
Chondrichthyes	Embryo	Adult	
Osteichthyes	Embryo	Adult	
Amphibia	Embryo	Adult	
Reptilia	Embryo	Embryo	Embryo and Adult
Aves	Embryo	Embryo	Embryo and Adult
Mammalia	Embryo	Embryo	Embryo and Adult

duct, which had been associated with the embryonic pronephros, extends forward, anterior to the mesonephros. Posteriorly, the two mesonephric ducts unite and open into a *urogenital sinus* which in turn leads to the outside. Two openings, the *genital pores,* connect the coelom with the urogenital sinus. Through these pores eggs and sperm pass from the coelom into the urogenital sinus and so to the outside. Hence, the urogenital sinus functions both as an excretory and as a genital structure.

Chondrichthyes and Osteichthyes. Pronephric tubules persist in a few adult teleosts. All other fishes have only the opistho-nephros present in the adult. The kidneys of fishes are dorsal in position. In some, such as the elasmobranchs, they are long, narrow, straplike bodies lying against the body wall under the peritoneum. In others, they are more bulky, while in some forms, they are rather short and confined to the posterior portion of the body cavity. Peritoneal funnels are for the most part absent, but they are present in the sturgeons and *Amia.* Although formed in the spiny dogfish, *Squalus acanthias,* they lose their connections with the renal tubules and end blindly. Some marine teleosts lack glomeruli; kidneys of this type are said to be *aglomerular.*

The opisthonephric kidneys of the non-teleost fishlike vertebrates tend to be longer in the male than in the female. The anterior end of the male opisthonephros is appropriated by the reproductive system. Modified kidney tubules, the *efferent ductules,* connect the gonad (testis) to the anterior end of the old archinephric duct, which is now called the *ductus deferens.* The teleost fishes lack a connection between the testis and the kidney. The duct from the testis either opens directly to the outside or joins the mesonephric or Wolffian duct near its posterior end. Thus, the *sperm duct* of these fishes is not homologous with that of the other vertebrates, in which it is formed from the old archinephric duct, and hence should not be called by the same name (ductus deferens).

Amphibia. The primitive, archinephric-type kidney occurs among the Amphibia only in larval Apoda, which have a metameric arrangement of the renal structures. The pronephros, or head kidney, is present in many larval amphibians, but never persists in the adult stage. Hence, the opisthonephros is the only functional kidney in adult amphibians.

The opisthonephric kidneys of salamanders and trachystomes are grossly similar in structure to those of the elasmobranchs. Two portions may be differentiated—a narrow, anterior portion, and a more expanded posterior portion. The narrow anterior portion of the males is concerned more with reproduction than with excretion. The expanded posterior portion comprises the bulk of the kidney and is entirely excretory in function. The mesonephric duct runs along the lateral edge of the kidney. The anterior end of this duct serves as the ductus deferens of the males in addition to transporting wastes.

Necturus has peritoneal connections between the coelom and the kidney tubules.

Among the frogs and toads, the opisthonephros shows a posterior concentration of renal structures and is confined to the more posterior portion of the abdominal cavity. The kidneys lie along the dorsal wall of the coelom beneath the peritoneum. There is no sharp distinction between anterior and posterior ends, and the mesonephric duct passes through the kidney rather than along its lateral margin as it does in salamanders and trachystomes. Male frogs have efferent ductules connecting the testis with the anterior portion of the mesonephric duct, which thus becomes a ductus deferens.

In the amphibians, a thin-walled urinary bladder develops as a bilobed evaginated sac from the ventral wall of the cloaca.

Urine thus passes from the mesonephric duct into the cloaca and thence to the bladder rather than from the mesonephric duct directly to the bladder.

Reptilia. The metanephros is the functional adult kidney. The pronephros appears only briefly, but the mesonephros exists for a time as a temporary structure prior to the development of the metanephros. It is functional in the embryo and may persist for a short time after hatching. With the development of the amniote metanephros, the mesonephric duct persists in the male in the form of such derived reproductive structures as the *epididymis* and *ductus deferens.*

There is some variation in the arrangement of the metanephric kidneys among the reptiles, correlated largely with variations of body form. In general, the kidneys of reptiles are rather compact, small, and lobulated. Snakes and the elongated, limbless lizards have elongated kidneys with extremely long ureters. On the other hand, turtles have very short ureters.

The ureters of reptiles open separately into the cloaca and have no direct connection with the bladder. Crocodilians and snakes lack a bladder, but *Sphenodon,* turtles, and most lizards have one which is formed partly from the cloaca and partly from the base of the embryonic allantoic membrane. Some turtles have an accessory pair of urinary bladders connected with the cloaca.

Aves. The pronephros and mesonephros are present only in the embryo. The metanephric kidneys are short, lobed structures lying in the pelvic region of the body cavity. In all the birds, the ureters open independently into the cloaca. With the single known exception of the ostrich, urinary bladders are lacking. The loop of Henle shows up for the first time among the birds.

Mammalia. Pronephric tubules appear only in the early stages of mammalian development. The mesonephros is reduced and is scarcely functional in some mammalian embryos, but in others it is a well developed organ. In the monotremes and some marsupials it may persist for a short time after birth. As with the other amniotes, the mesonephric ducts persist and give rise to such male reproductive structures as the ductus deferens, epididymis, and seminal vesicles. Traces of the Wolffian duct are also present in the female reproductive tract but are not functional.

The mammalian metanephric kidneys are rather compact, bean-shaped structures. They lie in the pelvic region of the abdomen, along the dorsal wall behind the peritoneum, and hence are said to be retroperitoneal. Well developed loops of Henle are present in the renal tubules between the proximal and distal convolutions. The mammalian kidney is usually divided into an outer portion, the *cortex,* containing the renal corpuscles and convoluted portions of the renal tubules, and an inner portion, the *medulla,* containing the collecting tubules and loops of Henle. The collecting tubules empty into a cavity, the *renal pelvis,* which is drained by the ureter.

Well developed urinary bladders are present in all mammals, and in all the bladder opens to the outside by means of a new tube, the *urethra.* The ureters of the egg-laying mammals (monotremes) open into the single urethra near the base of the bladder. The ureters of all other mammals open directly into the bladder, which in turn opens to the outside by means of the urethra. Flow of urine from the bladder through the urethra is controlled by a sphincter muscle at the mouth of the bladder.

A true cloaca is present in the monotremes, but in the higher mammals the embryonic cloaca becomes separated into distinct urogenital and digestive portions which have independent openings to the outside.

EXCRETION AND ENVIRONMENT

There are three main types of environments that vertebrates may inhabit: fresh water, salt water, and dry land. Each of these environments poses a different problem in regard to the regulation of the water and salt content of the body fluids.

Regulation of water content in fresh-water animals. Animals that live in fresh water are surrounded by a medium less concentrated than their body fluids, so there is a tendency for water to enter the body by osmosis. The problem is eliminating the excess water. It has been suggested that the ancestral vertebrate evolved in fresh water and that the glomerulus developed primarily as a mechanism for the elimination of water. Fresh-water fishes and amphibians have large glomeruli and relatively short tubules; they excrete copious amounts of dilute urine.

Regulation of water content in salt-water animals. The surrounding medium of animals that live in salt water is more concentrated than their body fluids and the tendency is for water to pass out of the body. Here the problem is conserving body water. In marine teleosts the glomeruli are reduced or absent and only a small amount of urine is formed. Much of the metabolic waste is excreted through the gills. The elasmobranchs retain the primitive large glomeruli and short tubules and excrete large amounts of dilute urine as do the fresh-water forms. The elasmobranchs, however, are able to reabsorb urea through the tubules. Large amounts of urea in the blood raise its osmotic level so that although the salt concentration in elasmobranchs is below that of sea water, the total osmotic value is about the same and water is not lost through the membranes.

Regulation of water content in terrestrial animals. The terrestrial reptiles, birds, and mammals are also in danger of losing too much water to the environment. Reptiles have small glomeruli and excrete small amounts of urine. They are also able to reabsorb some water through the cloacal bladder. Birds and mammals have large glomeruli, but the tubules are lengthened through the development of Henle's loop; much water is reabsorbed and the urine is much more concentrated than that of the amphibian.

Regulation of salt concentration. Loss of body water to the environment results in an increased concentration of salts in the blood. The problem of the maintenance of a proper salt balance is especially acute in marine animals since they ingest salt water with their food and may drink it. Sharks have a special gland in the rectum by which excess salt is excreted and the marine teleosts and lampreys excrete salt through the gills. Oceanic birds have a salt gland in the nasal cavity and sea turtles have similar glands in the orbit of the eye. Terrestrial mammals may excrete excess salt through the sweat glands.

11

Reproductive System

The reproductive system is concerned with the production of offspring and consequently with the maintenance of the race.

Three types of structures are involved in reproduction: (1) primary organs, the *gonads,* that produce the *gametes* or germ cells; (2) accessory organs, that have the function of bringing the gametes of one sex into contact with the gametes of the other sex (including such structures as the genital tubes and copulatory organs); and (3) secondary structures or characters that serve primarily in sex recognition (including such things as plumage, size, strength, voice, color, scent glands, etc.). The secondary sex structures of one group are not as a rule homologous with those of another group. (Since they are not really part of the reproductive system, they will not be described in this chapter.)

Much of the evolution of the reproductive system is closely associated with the evolution of the excretory system. This is particularly true in the males, for in them the same tubes may serve as excretory ducts and as accessory sex organs.

COMPARATIVE ANATOMY OF PRIMARY ORGANS

The primary sex organs of the female are the *ovaries;* those of the male are the *testes* (sing. *testis*).

Ovary. The ovaries of the vertebrates have two functions: a *cytogenic* one, by which the *ova* are formed and with which we are here concerned, and an *endocrinic* one, in which certain sex hormones are produced.

The ova are formed in the *germinal epithelium,* a thin layer of cells on the outer surface of the ovary. As each ovum develops, it becomes surrounded by a sheath of epithelial cells, the *ovarian* (or *Graafian*) *follicle*. When the ovum is mature, the follicle ruptures and the ovum is discharged into the coelom.

Agnatha. Two situations are found in the cyclostomes—one in the lampreys and the other in the hagfishes. The lampreys have two ovaries in the larval stage, one on each side of the dorsal mesentery. However, as the animal matures the dorsal mesentery breaks down and the larval ovaries meet and fuse on the midline. Thus, the adult female lamprey has a single gonad which runs the entire length of the body cavity and is attached to the mid-dorsal body wall by a sheet of peritoneum, the *mesovarium*.

The hagfishes, on the other hand, have a single median structure, as do the lampreys, but this structure, instead of being a simple ovary, is dual in nature. The anterior portion becomes ovarian, the posterior portion testicular; thus, the hagfish is *hermaphroditic*. In the adult hagfish, one or the other primary sex organ usually becomes predominant. The ripe eggs from the ovary in all the cyclostomes are shed directly into the coelom.

Chondrichthyes. The Chondrichthyes have paired, solid ovaries located in the anterior portion of the body cavity. Generally, both ovaries are functional; in a few elasmobranchs, however, only the right one becomes fully developed. The eggs are shed into the body cavity.

Osteichthyes. Most of the primitive actinopterygians and a few teleosts have solid ovaries and release their eggs directly into the coelom as do the Chondrichthyes. The great majority of the bony fishes have hollow, saccular ovaries and release their eggs into the cavity inside the ovary. The *oviduct*, which is simply a narrow continuation of the sac forming the ovary, leads posteriorly to the outside. Even here, though, we can say that the eggs are released into the coelom, since the saccular ovary of the teleost fish is so formed that its cavity is simply a pinched-off part of the cavity of the coelom. Hence, when eggs are extruded into this cavity, they are, in fact, really entering the coelom.

Amphibia. The amphibians have hollow ovaries, but their cavities are simply interstitial spaces and the structure of the gonad is different from that of the bony fishes. The shape of the amphibian ovary is somewhat irregular, particularly when it is filled with ripe ova. The ovaries may then fill up the greater part of the body cavity. The eggs are shed through the outer wall of the ovary directly into the coelom. Fat bodies, which apparently serve as a storage place for nutriments, are closely associated with the ovaries. A unique structure, *Bidder's organ*, present in the male toad (*Bufo*) may, under certain conditions, develop into a true cytogenic ovary.

Reptilia. Snakes and lizards have saccular ovaries like those of the amphibians, while turtles and crocodilians have more or less solid ovaries. In general, the ovaries of snakes and lizards are more elongate than those of other reptiles. They are not symmetrically placed in the snakes, which have the right ovary lying anterior to the left. The ovaries of the turtles and crocodilians are more compact in structure and are symmetrically placed. As in the amphibians, the eggs rupture through the outer wall of the ovary and pass directly into the body cavity. It should be pointed out here that only the gamete with its associated yolk is produced by the ovary; all additional materials of the egg, such as albumen and shell, are laid down in the oviduct.

Aves. Avian ovaries are solid and embryonically, at least, are paired structures. During the development of most birds, the right ovary degenerates and the left becomes the functional adult ovary. Experiments have shown, however, that in the domestic chicken the degenerate right ovary can develop into a testis-like structure if the functional left ovary is removed. The reduction from two to one functional ovary in the birds is apparently associated with reduction in weight, which, in turn, is associated with the flying habit.

Mammalia. Mammalian ovaries are generally rather small compared with the rest of the body. They are solid, somewhat compact structures and are paired, although the left ovary of the egg-laying mammals is much better developed than is the right and, according to one authority, is the only functional one. As in the other tetrapods, the mammalian eggs rupture through the outer wall of the ovary into the body cavity; however, in many mammals the opening of the oviduct is so closely invested around the ovary that there is little chance for the ova to do anything except pass directly into the oviduct.

Testis. As with the female ovary, the male testis is dual in function: cytogenic in that it produces the male gametes, or *sperm,* and endocrinic in that it produces sex hormones.

The typical testis is a rather compact organ somewhat variable in shape among the different groups of vertebrates. In all except a few of the lower forms, it is essentially a mass of *seminiferous tubules* connected by means of ducts to the outside. The cells in the walls of the seminiferous tubules give rise to the spermatozoa. The testes of most vertebrates are paired structures located in the dorsal portion of the body cavity where they first appear during embryonic development. In most mammals, however, they later migrate into a special, pouchlike structure, the *scrotum.*

Agnatha. As with the ovaries, two conditions of the testes are found in the cyclostomes. The lamprey testis differs but little in appearance from the ovary. It is an unpaired structure lying along the mid-dorsal body wall; like the median ovary, it represents a fusion of two embryonic structures. The sperm cells break through the outer wall of the testis and are shed directly into the coelom.

As has already been mentioned (p. 122), the hagfish gonad is really part ovarian and part testicular; hence the animal is hermaphroditic.

Chondrichthyes. The testes of the cartilaginous fishes are paired, more or less symmetrical structures located in the anterior end of the body cavity. They vary in shape from rather oval to somewhat elongated; they increase in size prior to the breeding season and grow smaller after its close.

Osteichthyes. The testis of the bony fishes resembles that of the cartilaginous fishes except that it tends to be more elongated and often may be somewhat lobular as well. The testes of some of the commercial fishes are eaten as "white roe."

Amphibia. Among the amphibians the main variation in the testis concerns the shape, which is closely associated with the form of the body. Thus, the testes of the caecilians are elongated and in general appearance somewhat like strings of beads. Salamander testes are shorter and more irregular in outline, while in the frogs and toads the testes are rather compact, bean-shaped structures. As with the ovaries, fat bodies are associated with the testes of the amphibians.

Reptilia. The testes of the reptiles are rather compact structures. In the turtles and crocodilians they are symmetrically placed, but in the elongate snakes and lizards there is a pronounced tendency for one testis to lie anterior to the other.

Aves. The structure of the testis is rather uniform among the birds. It is characteristically a round or oval organ. The testes of some birds, such as the domestic fowl, show little seasonal variation in size, whereas in other birds there is quite a marked variation correlated with the breeding season.

Mammalia. The mammalian testis is a mass of convoluted seminiferous tubules surrounded by a tough, fibrous envelope, the *tunica albuginea*. Although the testis itself is rather small, the tubules are so numerous and so compactly arranged that their combined length is very great. The combined length of the tubules of the bull, for example, has been estimated to be several miles!

The testes of the monotremes lie in the anterior part of the body cavity, but those of all the other mammals descend to the pelvic region, where they may remain permanently or may further descend into the scrotum, a sac formed by an outpouching of the body wall. The testes of the elephants, sea cows, and whales remain permanently in the abdominal cavity. In the Chiroptera and in most rodents and some other mammals, the testes migrate periodically from the abdomen to the scrotum and back again. The testes of carnivores, artiodactyls, perissodactyls, primates, and a few others, descend into the scrotum and remain there throughout life. Occasionally among animals in which the testes descend into the scrotum, one or both remain abnormally in the abdominal cavity; such a testis is said to be *cryptorchid*. If the cryptorchidism is unilateral, the single scrotal testis may function normally. However, if bilateral cryptorchidism occurs, the animal is sterile.

COMPARATIVE ANATOMY OF THE ACCESSORY REPRODUCTIVE ORGANS

Among the vertebrates, accessory reproductive structures vary from simple abdominal pores to quite complex tubelike structures and finally to well developed copulatory organs.

It should be mentioned that in some of the vertebrates, particularly the amphibians and reptiles, the accessory ducts of one sex may appear as quite obvious structures in the other sex. Thus, the typically female *Müllerian ducts* are readily seen in some male frogs and lizards. The Müllerian ducts of the European wall lizard may be as well developed in the male as they are in the female.

Female Accessory Organs. The ovarian ducts of the females of most vertebrates are the Müllerian ducts.

Agnatha. Reproductive ducts are lacking in the cyclostomes. The eggs make their way from the coelom through *genital pores* into the urogenital sinus and thence out through an aperture at the tip of the *urogenital papilla.* External fertilization occurs in the cyclostomes.

Chondrichthyes. The oviduct of the Chondrichthyes differs from the typical Müllerian duct. It seems to be formed by a pinching off of part of the original archinephric duct, whereas the Müllerian duct of the higher vertebrates is formed by the pinching off of a groove in the peritoneum adjacent to the Wolffian duct. Nevertheless, rather definite homologies are thought to exist between the Müllerian duct in the Chondrichthyes and in the tetrapods. In the Chondrichthyes the Müllerian ducts fuse at their anterior ends so that there is a single opening, or *ostium tubae,* connecting with the coelom.

Shell glands are present in the ducts of all elasmobranchs, and hence fertilization is always internal, since it is essential that sperm enter the egg before a shell is deposited around it. Posterior to the shell gland is an expanded portion of the oviduct, the *uterus,* which opens into the cloaca. In some of the elasmobranchs, including the common laboratory dogfish, *Squalus acanthias,* the shell is a temporary structure which later breaks down. In these fishes development takes place within the uterus and the young are "born alive."

Osteichthyes. There is a remarkable amount of variation in the structure of the female ducts in the Osteichthyes. In the dipnoans, the oviducts are long, coiled, paired structures which are true Müllerian ducts. The saccular ovaries of most of the bony fishes have short oviducts which are simply continuations of the gonads and are not true Müllerian ducts at all. Sometimes the two oviducts fuse posteriorly to form a single duct which leads to the outside by means of a genital pore. Among those fishes in which the ovaries are solid and the eggs are shed into the coelom, short, funnel-like oviducts lead to the outside, but it is questionable whether these represent true Müllerian ducts.

Amphibia. The structure of the oviducts is rather uniform throughout the amphibians. They are always true Müllerian ducts. The oviducts of the common toad (*Bufo*) fuse posteriorly to form a single common duct, but in other amphibians they remain paired throughout their length and open separately into the cloaca. The Müllerian duct of the amphibians is glandular and secretes a gelatinous material around the eggs as they pass down the duct from the ovary on their way to the outside.

Reptilia. Reptilian oviducts are true Müllerian ducts and are differentiated into rather distinct sections. They all open into the coelom by means of slitlike ostia and are paired throughout their length. In turtles, crocodilians, and *Sphenodon,* albuminous glands are present in the anterior portion of the duct. Snakes and lizards lack well developed albuminous glands, and hence albumen is lacking around the eggs of these forms.

Posterior to the albuminous glands, shell glands are present in the Müllerian ducts of reptiles. The shell of most of the oviparous forms is of a parchment-like consistency, but in some of the lizards and in the crocodilians it is rather rigid and hard like that of a bird's egg. The ducts enter the cloaca separately. Fertilization is invariably internal among the reptiles.

Aves. Most birds have only a single, functional oviduct, the left; the right one is degenerate. The left duct is a long, coiled structure which, like that of the reptiles, is divided into rather distinct regions. As the egg passes down the oviduct the various layers of albumen, the shell membrane, and the shell itself are deposited around it. As in all animals that lay shelled eggs, fertilization must be internal. The oviduct opens into the cloaca.

Mammalia. The Müllerian duct of the monotremes is differentiated into a narrow, coiled anterior portion, the *Fallopian tube,* and an expanded, straight, posterior portion, the *uterus.* The two uteri open separately into the cloaca. Apparently, only the left oviduct is functional, in correlation with the single functional ovary. The right duct is present but non-functional. In other mammals, the Müllerian ducts are differentiated into three portions, the Fallopian tube (sometimes known as the oviduct), the uterus, and, posterior to the uterus, a terminal *vagina* which receives the penis during copulation. The vaginas of the marsupials open separately into the urogenital sinus. Sometimes the marsupial vaginas are fused at their anterior ends to form a single *vaginal sinus* which extends posteriorly as a blind pouch.

In the eutherian mammals, the vaginas are fused into a single structure and the uteri may be more or less fused as well. Many of the rodents and some of the bats have two completely separate uteri (a *duplex uterus*), while the apes and man have a single uterus (*simplex uterus*). Other mammals show intermediate degrees of fusion and have *bipartite* or *bicornuate* uteri.

Male Accessory Organs. The male accessory organs include the genital ducts and, for many forms, special copulatory organs.

Genital Duct. The genital duct of the male vertebrate usually originates as the archinephric duct. It serves also as the duct of the pronephric kidney and then as the mesonephric or Wolffian duct of the mesonephros or opisthonephros.

When efferent ductules carrying sperm from the testis enter the Wolffian duct, it becomes known as the *ductus deferens.* The end of the duct nearest the testis may become very much convoluted to form the *epididymis.* Persistent mesonephric tubules connect the epididymis with the seminiferous tubules of the testis. Sometimes an enlargement for the temporary storage of sperm, a *seminal vesicle,* forms near the posterior end of the duct. The seminal vesicle of mammals is a glandular diverticulum of the duct and is not generally used for sperm storage.

AGNATHA. The cyclostome males, like the females, lack genital ducts. The sperm, which have been released by the testis into the body cavity, leave through the genital pores.

CHONDRICHTHYES. In the Chondrichthyes, small efferent ductules pass from the testis through its supporting membrane to connect with anterior kidney tubules along the border of the opisthonephros. Thus, sperm are transferred from the testis into the Wolffian duct and the Wolffian duct becomes the ductus deferens.

OSTEICHTHYES. There is variation in the ducts of the Osteichthyes. The male duct of many of the bony fishes is entirely different in origin from the Wolffian duct. A separate tube formed from folds of peritoneum connects the gonad to the urogenital sinus, and hence the duct is not homologous to the Wolffian duct. However, in some of the primitive fishes, the sturgeon for example, the efferent ductules do lead into the Wolffian duct, which in these fishes is a true ductus deferens.

AMPHIBIA. The efferent ductules of the amphibian testis may either lead directly through the kidney into the Wolffian duct (ductus deferens) or they may join to form a *Bidder's canal* from which tubules pass through the kidney to join the Wolffian duct.

REPTILIA, AVES, MAMMALIA. Since the reptiles, birds and mammals have developed a metanephros with a new excretory tube, the ureter, the old mesonephric duct serves only as a ductus deferens. The ductus deferens of most reptiles joins the ureter so that the two enter the cloaca through a common aperture. In birds the ductus deferens and ureter enter the cloaca separately, while in mammals the duct joins the urethra a short way below the bladder.

Copulatory Structures. Internal fertilization is mandatory for animals that lay shelled eggs and also for those in which development is initiated within the oviduct. It is generally achieved by means of copulation, in which the male places the sperm in the reproductive tract of the female. Special copulatory organs have been evolved independently a number of times in various groups of vertebrates.

CHONDRICHTHYES. The pelvic fins of the elasmobranchs are modified as copulatory organs; processes on these paired fins serve to inject the sperm into the cloaca of the female.

OSTEICHTHYES. Most fishes have external fertilization and hence lack copulatory organs, but in some of them the anal fin is modified as a copulatory structure. The genital opening of the female of one of the small, tropical fishes is covered by a large scale which sometimes is hinged on the right side and sometimes on the left. Since copulation can only occur on the unhinged side, the males have been modified into right- and left-handed types so far as their copulatory structures are concerned. Right-handed males mate with left-handed females and vice versa.

AMPHIBIA. The cloaca of the male caecilians is protrusible and serves as a copulatory organ. This same condition is found in one of the frogs, though most frogs have external fertilization. Fertilization is internal in most of the salamanders, but no copulation is involved. The male deposits a *spermatophore,* a packet of sperm on a jelly-like base. The female picks it up with the lips of her cloaca and thereby the sperm are transferred from the male to the female.

REPTILIA. *Sphenodon* lacks a copulatory organ and transfer of sperm is brought about by cloacal apposition. Snakes and lizards have a pair of eversible copulatory organs, the *hemipenes.* Turtles and crocodilians have a true penis—a single, erectile, copulatory organ homologous to that of the mammals. Sperm are transmitted through a groove on its dorsal surface.

AVES. Most birds lack copulatory organs and transfer the sperm by cloacal apposition. Ducks, geese, swans, and ostriches have a small penis similar structurally to that of the crocodilians.

MAMMALIA. Mammals also have a single, erectile penis. The groove on the dorsal surface has closed over to form a tube. The penis of the monotremes is housed in the cloaca. Since in them the urethra has a separate opening into the cloaca, it is believed that only sperm pass through the tube of the penis. In males of other mammals, the deferent ducts join the urethra and both sperm and urine pass through the tube of the penis. The penis of the marsupials and rabbits is posterior to the scrotum rather than anterior, as it is in the higher mammals. Among the placental mammals, the penis is sheathed in all except primates. A bony structure, the *os penis*, is embedded in the penis of rodents, carnivores, and bats.

12

Circulatory System

The circulatory system of the vertebrates can be divided into two portions: the blood-vascular system and the lymphatic system. Although they are both associated with the flow of fluids through the body, they will be considered separately.

BLOOD-VASCULAR SYSTEM

The blood-vascular system is made up of: (1) a muscular pump, the _heart;_ (2) a series of _arteries_—vessels that carry blood away from the heart; (3) _capillaries_—little, thin-walled vessels usually at the terminations of the arteries; and (4) _veins_—vessels that collect blood and carry it back to the heart. All of these vessels are lined with a layer of epithelial cells called _endothelium._ Also in the vertebrate body are _sinusoids_, spaces in tissues through which the blood passes but which are not lined with endothelium. Such sinusoids may be found in the spleen, liver, and pancreas.

Origin and Structure of Blood-Vascular System. The entire blood-vascular system originates from small clumps of cells, the _blood islands,_ which develop in the mesoderm and subsequently grow and become confluent to form blood vessels.

Heart. The vertebrate heart is a muscular chamber divided into a series of compartments. The blood islands that give rise to the heart form in the splanchnic hypomere and the heart is formed _in situ_ below the gut. In animals with holoblastic cleavage, the heart develops directly in the ventral mesentery, while in animals with meroblastic cleavage, paired _vitelline veins_ first appear from the blood islands and subsequently fuse along the midline to form the heart.

Like the blood vessels, the heart is lined with an endothelial layer, here called endocardium. Surrounding this is a thick layer of cardiac muscle, the myocardium. The heart is covered by a thin membrane, the epicardium.

Blood Vessels. Typically, the walls of blood vessels are made up of three coats or tunics, as follows: a *tunica interna,* or *intima,* composed of endothelium and elastic tissue; a *tunica media* of circular, smooth muscles; and a *tunica externa,* or *adventitia,* of connective tissue and longitudinally-arranged collagenous and elastic fibers. The degree to which these tunics are developed differs in the different kinds of vessels.

ARTERIES. These are the blood vessels that carry blood away from the heart. Arterial walls are made up of well developed tunics, and consequently the arteries are thick-walled vessels.

VEINS. The veins, which carry blood toward the heart, are comprised primarily of the tunica externa, with the other tunics less well developed than in the arteries; consequently, they are essentially thin-walled vessels which tend to collapse when not distended by blood. The veins further differ from the arteries in that they may have valves in their walls to prevent the backward flow of blood.

CAPILLARIES. The capillaries, the smallest vessels in the body, are made up primarily of endothelium. In a normal, functioning body, they are the only blood vessels from which the fluid portion of the blood can pass through the wall; hence, it is only in capillary beds that there is an actual exchange of material between the blood and the tissue fluid surrounding the cells.

Arrangement of Blood-Vascular System. Typically, the arteries carrying blood away from the heart terminate in capillaries, and these capillaries recombine to form the veins which carry blood back to the heart. This arrangement, however, is not the only one found in the vertebrates.

The portal systems differ in that here the veins break down into capillaries that recombine into veins. There are a maximum of three of these systems in the vertebrate body: a hepatic portal system; a renal portal system; and a pituitary system. The hepatic and renal portal systems are particularly significant and will be discussed in detail under the comparative anatomy of the venous system.

Conversely, arteries may break down into capillaries and these capillaries recombine into arteries instead of veins. This situation is found in the kidney, in which the afferent artery going into a glomerulus divides into the capillaries of the glomerulus proper. These capillaries unite to form the efferent artery leading away from the glomerulus. A similar arrangement occurs in certain structures called *red bodies* associated with the swim bladder and occasionally with the coelom proper in certain aquatic vertebrates.

Finally, it should be mentioned that occasionally arteries may lead directly into veins without an intervening capillary bed (*arteriovenous anastomoses*). This is particularly true in the distal portion of appendages which may be exposed to extremes of low temperature such as the tips of the fingers, the lips, nose, eyelids, the ear of the rabbit, etc. This arrangement simply facilitates blood flow for transporting the maximum amount of heat into these appendages in the minimum amount of time.

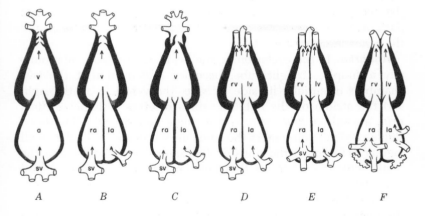

Fig. 12-1. Comparative anatomy of the vertebrate heart. A, elasmobranch; B, lungfish and salamander; C, frog; D, lower reptile; E, alligator; F, bird and mammal. V, ventricle; a, atrium; sv, sinus venosus. (After Kingsley.)

Comparative Anatomy of the Vertebrate Heart. Primitively, the vertebrate heart consists of two main chambers: the *atrium* and the *ventricle*; and two accessory chambers: the *sinus venosus* and the *conus arteriosus*. In higher forms, the conus and sinus are lost. Hence, only the atrium and the ventricle are considered true heart chambers and the primitive heart is spoken of as a *two-chambered heart.* In higher vertebrates, the atrium and ventricle may be divided by partitions to form a *four-chambered heart.*

The heart tube develops sequentially from front to rear, and as it is developing it begins to beat. The most anterior part of the heart is the conus arteriosus, which empties into a large artery leading anteriorly—the *ventral aorta* or *truncus arteriosus.* Posterior to the conus, the ventricle develops. The initial contractions of the heart take place in what will form the muscular layer of the ventricle, the *ventricular myocardium.* Behind this ventricular myocardium the initial atrium develops, which again starts to pulsate as soon as it is established. It is interesting to note that the atrium pulsates faster than does the ventricle, and that as soon as its pulsations start, the ventricle increases its rate to keep pace with the atrium. Posterior to the atrium the sinus venosus develops. This beats still faster and the ventricle and atrium step up their rates to coincide with it. Thus, the four portions of the primitive heart are, from anterior to posterior: the conus arteriosus, the ventricle, the atrium, and the sinus venosus (Fig. 12-1).

Agnatha. In the cyclostomes, the heart, which was embryonically a simple, straight tube, becomes folded so that the two chambers essentially lie side by side—the ventricle on the right and the atrium on the left. The sinus receives a single *cardinal vein,* a single *jugular vein,* and a single *hepatic vein.* The large single cardinal vein enters the sinus on the dorsal side; the small jugular vein enters the sinus on the antero-ventral side; and the small hepatic vein enters the sinus on the posterior side. Blood flows from the sinus into the atrium and thence into the ventricle. It is then forced from the ventricle through the conus into the ventral aorta and is distributed to the gills. Valves in the openings between the heart chambers prevent the backflow of blood; between the sinus and atrium are the *sinoatrial valves* and between the atrium and ventricle are the *atrioventricular valves.* The small conus of the cyclostomes is equipped with a single set of *semilunar valves.*

The circulatory system of the cyclostomes is a *single-type circulatory system;* only a single stream of unoxygenated blood passes through the heart.

Chondrichthyes. The arrangement of the elasmobranch heart is essentially the same as that of the cyclostomes. The sinus venosus now receives paired *hepatic veins* bringing blood from the liver and paired *Cuvierian ducts* (*common cardinal veins*) bringing blood from the rest of the body. The conus arteriosus is better developed and has a series of valves in three longitudinal rows. In some elasmobranchs, there may be as many as six sets of valves. Like the cyclostomes, the Chondrichthyes have a single-type circulatory system with only unoxygenated blood passing through the heart.

Osteichthyes. The structure of the heart of most of the bony fishes is essentially like that of the cartilaginous fishes. However, the Dipnoi (lung fishes) show a specialization from the two-chambered to three-chambered heart. In these animals, a central partition develops in the atrium, partially dividing it into right and left chambers. The sinus venosus empties into the right chamber, while oxygenated blood coming from the lung enters by means of a *pulmonary vein* into the left atrium. Furthermore, the ventricle itself is partially separated into right and left halves by an incomplete septum which is made up of fibrous and muscular tissue and which tends to prevent mixing of the oxygenated and unoxygenated blood in the ventricle. In *Protopterus,* the conus itself is divided into right and left halves so that the two streams of blood, the oxygenated on the left and the unoxygenated on the right, leave the heart separately. The oxygenated blood goes to the anterior gill region and thence directly to the dorsal aorta, while the unoxygenated blood goes to the posterior gill region and much of it passes to the lung. Thus, in this group, for the first time, we have the beginning of a double-type circulatory system, although the two types of blood are not here completely separated, and indeed they are never completely separated in any ectothermal vertebrate.

Amphibia. In the Caudata, as in the dipnoans, the atrium is divided into right and left halves by an *interatrial septum.* The ventricle is undivided so that the Caudata have a three-chambered heart. The sinus venosus enters the right atrium, the sinus itself being supplied by right and left ducts of Cuvier (now called *precaval veins*) and by a posterior *postcaval vein*. A pulmonary vein from the lungs enters the left atrium in all except the lungless salamanders of the family Plethodontidae and one Asiatic lungless form. In them there is no blood vessel to enter the left atrium, but there is a large aperture in the interatrial septum so that the two atrial chambers are continuous with one another.

The blood passes from the two atria into the single ventricle and then forward through the conus into the ventral aorta.

The heart of the frogs and toads is similar to that of the salamanders except that the conus has a structure called the *spiral valve* which keeps the blood that has come from the right atrium somewhat separate from that which has come from the left atrium. The oxygenated blood from the left atrium tends to pass through the ventricle and up through the anterior branches of the ventral aorta to the brain. The blood from the right atrium passes through the ventricle and then through the posterior branches of the ventral aorta, including the *pulmocutaneous artery* which carries blood to the lungs and skin for aeration.

Reptilia. Pronounced changes have taken place in the structure of the reptilian heart as compared to that of the amphibians. In the first place, only the turtles have a discrete sinus. In all other forms the sinus has become embedded in the wall of the right atrium. The interatrial septum is complete and an *interventricular septum* is formed, at least in part, in all the reptiles and is complete in the crocodilians, which thus have a true four-chambered heart.

The pulmonary veins enter the left atrium and the precaval and postcaval veins enter the right atrium. Thus the left side of the heart has oxygenated blood and the right side unoxygenated; there is not much mixing of the two streams even when the interventricular septum is incomplete. The conus is lacking and the truncus leading anterior from the ventricle divides at its base into three main trunks: a *pulmonary trunk* and a *right systemic trunk* from the right side of the ventricle, and a *left systemic trunk* from the left side. Each has a row of *semilunar valves* at its base. The two systemic trunks cross after leaving the heart so that the right trunk gives rise to the *left aortic arch* and the left trunk gives rise to the *right aortic arch*. Crocodilians have an opening, the *foramen Panizzae,* between the two systemic trunks at the point at which they cross so that even though the interventricular septum is complete, there is not an absolute separation between the oxygenated blood from the left side of the heart and the unoxygenated blood from the right side. Small *coronary arteries* bring blood to the heart muscle.

Aves. A complete double circulatory system, in which the pulmonary circulation is entirely separate from the systemic circulation, appears in the birds for the first time. The sinus has disappeared completely. The interatrial septum and the interventricular septum are complete. A single trunk, the pulmonary, leaves the right ventricle. Thus, all the unoxygenated blood from the body enters the right atrium, flows into the right ventricle and is passed of necessity to the lungs. On the left side of the heart, the pulmonary veins carrying oxygenated blood enter the left atrium, from which the blood passes to the left ventricle, out the single *systemic aortic trunk* leaving the left ventricle, and so to the body. Auxiliary out-pocketings known as *auricles* develop from the walls of the atria. These pouches simply function as reservoirs. Coronory arteries are well developed.

Mammalia. Structurally, the heart of the mammals is very similar to that of the birds. As in the birds, a complete double circulatory heart is present. The sinus is gone, and the truncus now forms only two trunks, namely, the pulmonary coming from the right ventricle and going to the lungs, and the systemic coming from the left ventricle and going by way of an arch to the dorsal aorta. Auricles are well developed.

Comparative Anatomy of Aortic Arches. The story of the evolution of the aortic arches among the vertebrates is a fascinating one which can be closely correlated with the evolution of the behavior and life habits of the vertebrates themselves, particularly in regard to the change from an aquatic to a terrestrial existence. Despite the complexities of the various patterns shown by the aortic arches, all of the conditions can apparently be derived from a simple primitive situation.

In the primitive, hypothetical animal, the ventral aorta gave rise to a series of paired branches, the *aortic arches,* which led up through the visceral arches around the pharynx to a pair of *radices* above the pharynx. These radices continued posteriorly to join and form the single *dorsal aorta.* Continuations of the ventral aorta anteriorly beyond the first aortic arches formed the primitive *external carotid arteries* to the lower jaw. The continuations of the radices of the dorsal aorta beyond the first arches formed the primitive *internal carotid arteries* to the brain and upper part of the head. From this primitive pattern all patterns of aortic arches among the vertebrates may be derived.

Cyclostomes and a few primitive sharks have more than six pairs of aortic arches. All other vertebrates show traces of six pairs during embryonic development. Hence, six is considered the typical primitive vertebrate number of aortic arches. These are numbered from anterior to posterior and are usually designated by Roman numerals (Fig. 12-2).

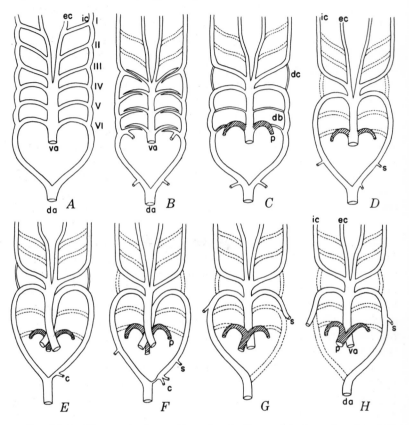

FIG. 12-2. Changes in the aortic arches in the vertebrate series. A, primitive condition; B, lungfish; C, salamander; D, frog; E, snake; F, lizard; G, bird; H, mammal; ec, external carotid; ic, internal carotid; da, dorsal aorta; va, ventral aorta; dc, ductus caroticus; db, ductus Botalli or ductus arteriosus; p, pulmonary; s, subclavian; c, coeliac. (After Kingsley.)

The aortic arches of the fishlike vertebrates are interrupted by capillary beds in the region of the gills. Each arch comprises an *afferent branchial artery*, the capillary network, and an *efferent branchial artery*.

Agnatha. The number of aortic arches in the cyclostomes varies from species to species. One species of myxinoid, *Bdellostoma stouti,* has fifteen pairs. The sea lamprey, *Petromyzon marinus,* has eight pairs.

Chondrichthyes. The first aortic arch, though present embryonically, is absent in most adult Chondrichthyes. The second, third, fourth, fifth, and sixth form the afferent branchial arteries which pass to the gills and break up into capillaries. These capillaries unite to form the efferent branchial arteries which join the radices of the dorsal aorta. External and internal carotids are formed as in the hypothetical primitive pattern.

Osteichthyes. Typically, the bony fishes have lost the first two arches, and the third, fourth, fifth, and sixth form the afferent and efferent branchial arteries. Among the Dipnoi, a pulmonary artery arises from the efferent portion of the sixth arch.

Amphibia. The amphibians show some variation, but basically two major patterns are found. The aortic arches are not broken into afferent and efferent portions. In the salamanders, as in the fishes, the first and second arches have disappeared. The third forms the carotid arch which gives rise to the internal carotid artery of the head. The fourth arch becomes the main systemic arch carrying blood to the dorsal aorta. The fifth arch is still present but is reduced in size. The sixth arch gives rise to the *pulmocutaneous* artery. The portion of the sixth arch between the pulmocutaneous artery and the radix of the aorta is now known as the *ductus Botalli (ductus arteriosus).* A remnant of the radix of the aorta between the third (or carotid) and the fourth (or systemic) arch, known as the *ductus caroticus,* may persist in the salamanders. As in the fishlike forms, the two radices of the aorta come together posteriorly to form the single, median dorsal aorta.

The anurans differ from the salamanders. As before, the first two aortic arches have disappeared. The third forms the carotid, the fourth forms the systemic arch, but in adults the fifth has disappeared, and the sixth is complete only to the pulmocutaneous artery. The adult frog has lost the ductus Botalli and the ductus caroticus.

Reptilia. The reptiles also show some variation in the aortic arches. The first and second arches are lost. It will be recalled (see p. 136) that the ventral aorta has divided at its base into three trunks which open separately from the ventricle. The systemic trunk coming from the left side of the ventricle gives off the *fourth right aortic arch.* Anterior to this it divides into the two *common carotid arteries.* Each of these again divides into the external carotid, representing the anterior extension of the ventral aorta, and the internal carotid, representing the third aortic arch. The systemic trunk coming from the right side of the ventricle crosses over the one from the left side to lead to the left *fourth aortic arch,* and the left and right fourth aortic arches unite to form the dorsal aorta. (A remnant of the ductus caroticus may be present in certain snakes.)

The fifth aortic arches are usually lost but may be present, though reduced, in some lizards. The pulmonary trunk coming from the right side of the ventricle divides into right and left pulmonary arteries, representing the sixth aortic arches. A remnant of the ductus Botalli persists in *Sphenodon* and some turtles.

Aves. Reduction in the number of arches continues in the birds. The first, second, and fifth arches are gone. Two trunks leave the heart: the systemic from the left ventricle and the pulmonary from the right. At its anterior end the systemic divides into the carotids as in the reptiles. Only the right fourth aortic arch is complete; it alone forms the dorsal aorta. The base of the left fourth forms the base of the left *subclavian artery* going to the fore limb, but it has lost its connection with the dorsal aorta. The pulmonary trunk from the right ventricle gives rise to the pulmonary arteries, representing the ventral ends of the sixth arches. The ductus Botalli does not persist beyond the embryonic stage.

Mammalia. The arrangement of the aortic arches in the mammals is a mirror image of that found in the birds. The fourth left forms the systemic arch, with the fourth right forming the base of the right subclavian. As in the birds, the first, second, and fifth arches have disappeared in the adult, as have the ductus caroticus and the ductus Botalli.

Branches of Dorsal Aorta. There is not much to tell in the story of the comparative anatomy of the branches of the dorsal aorta among the vertebrates, for the dorsal aorta and its branches are essentially the same in all groups. The branches of the dorsal aorta may be divided into two major groups—the *somatic* and the *visceral.*

Somatic Branches of Dorsal Aorta. The somatic branches in general comprise a pair of *parietal arteries* for each body segment. In those vertebrates that have paired appendages, a number of parietals have fused to form the arteries for these appendages, namely, the *subclavian arteries* for the anterior appendages and the *iliac arteries* for the posterior appendages. The dorsal aorta continues into the tail as the *caudal artery*.

Visceral Branches of Dorsal Aorta. The visceral arteries include both unpaired and paired vessels. While there is some variation in the names used in the different groups of vertebrates, the pattern is essentially the same in all. Most vertebrates have as unpaired visceral arteries, (from anterior to posterior): a *coeliac*, a *superior mesenteric*, and an *inferior mesenteric*. The paired visceral arteries include the *renal arteries* going to the kidneys and, posterior to them, the *gonadal arteries* going to the gonads.

Venous System. The history of the venous system in the various groups of vertebrates is a complicated one, but there is a rather definite pattern which may be comprehended with a reasonable amount of effort.

Pattern of Venous System. There seems to be a basic embryonic pattern from which the venous system of all vertebrates may be derived. Leading into the sinus venosus from the anterior part of the body are a pair of *inferior jugular veins* from the jaws and lower portion of the face, and a pair of *anterior cardinal veins* from the head region. Also entering the sinus from each side are a pair of *lateral abdominal veins* (which come from the sides of the body wall) and a pair of *postcardinal veins* (which run from a loop around the anus through the dorsal portion of the coelom

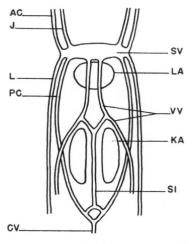

Fig. 12-3. The basic pattern of the venous system in vertebrates. AC, anterior cardinal; J, jugular; L, lateral; PC, postcardinal; CV, caudal vein; SV, sinus venosus; LA, liver anlage; VV, vitelline vein; KA, kidney anlage; SI, subintestinal.

to the sinus). A *caudal vein* from the tail joins the loop around the anus. A pair of *vitelline veins* from the yolk sac converge from the right and left sides and pass forward to enter the sinus from the region where the liver will develop. A *subintestinal vein* runs forward from the anal loop and divides into two branches which enter the right and left vitelline veins (Fig. 12-3).

Portal Systems. As was mentioned earlier, two very important portal systems, the hepatic and the renal, are included in the venous system. A comprehension of how these are developed is necessary for an understanding of the evolution of the venous system. Hence, we will trace the development of these two systems prior to our study of the comparative anatomy of the

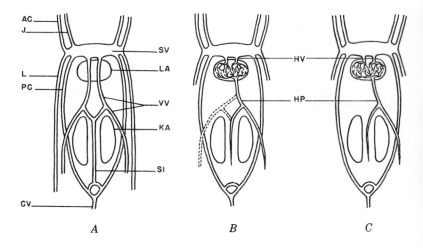

A   *B*   *C*

Fig. 12-4. The formation of the hepatic portal system in vertebrates. The main components are formed from the left vitelline and the subintestinal veins. HV, hepatic vein; HP, hepatic portal vein; other letters as in Fig. 12-3. (See text for details of changes between primitive condition in *A* and mature hepatic portal system in *C*.)

venous system proper. It should be remembered that a portal system has been defined as a part of the venous system that both originates and terminates in capillaries. There are three of these portal systems in the vertebrate body: the *pituitary*, the *hepatic*, and the *renal*. Only the two latter will concern us in our study of the comparative anatomy of the venous system.

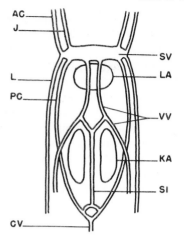

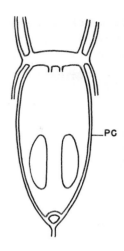

A

B

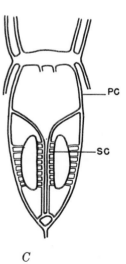

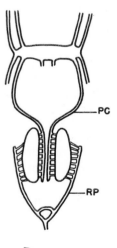

C

D

FIG. 12-5. The formation of the renal portal system in vertebrates. SC, subcardinal; RP, renal portal vein; AC, anterior cardinal; J, jugular; L, lateral; PC, postcardinal; CV, caudal vein; SV,
sinus venosus; LA, liver anlage; VV, vitelline vein, KA, kidney
anlage; SI, subintestinal. For clarity, the components of the
hepatic portal system are omitted in *B*, *C*, and *D*. (See text for
details of changes between primitive condition in *A* and mature
renal portal system in *D*.)

HEPATIC PORTAL SYSTEM. The formation of the hepatic portal system involves, basically, nothing more than a disintegration of certain veins and an interruption of others with capillary beds. The right vitelline and the right branch of the subintestinal disintegrate posterior to the liver. The left vitelline and part of the old subintestinal persist as the *hepatic portal vein* which leads into the liver and then breaks down into capillaries. A pair of vessels, now called *hepatic veins,* lead from the capillary bed of the liver into the posterior wall of the sinus venosus. Thus, the hepatic portal vein is made up of part of the old left vitelline plus part of the subintestinal, and the hepatic veins are made up of the anterior ends of the old vitelline veins (Fig. 12-4). All vertebrates have hepatic portal systems.

RENAL PORTAL SYSTEM. The structure of the renal portal system may be derived from the same primitive pattern as the hepatic portal system (Fig. 12-5A). In looking at the development of the renal portal system, we need concern ourselves only with the postcardinal veins at this point. These paired vessels lead from the anal loop anteriorly along the dorsal wall of the coelom to enter the right and left sides of the sinus (Fig. 12-5B). As they pass along the lateral margins of the developing kidneys, they form capillary connections with the kidneys. A new pair of vessels, the *subcardinals,* develop between the two kidneys. These vessels pass anteriorly from the anal loop and swing out to join the postcardinals anterior to the kidneys.

Once the subcardinals have formed, they also develop capillary connections with the kidneys (Fig. 12-5C). At this point, then, blood coming from the anal loop may actually flow in either direction through the capillary bed of the kidney. It may flow from the postcardinal through the kidney into the subcardinal, or from the subcardinal through the kidney into the postcardinal. Once the blood flow path from the postcardinal to the subcardinal has been developed, that portion of the postcardinal between the point where the subcardinal joins it and the anterior end of the kidney disintegrates. Usually, the part of the subcardinal between the anal loop and the kidney also disintegrates (Fig. 12-5D). Hence, the blood is now forced to flow from the posterior remnant of the postcardinal through the capillary bed of the kidney into the subcardinal, then on through the anterior portion of the postcardinal and thence to the heart. We now call the blood vessel running from the anal loop up the lateral margin of the kidney the *renal portal vein.* We call the small veins leading from the capillaries of the kidney to the subcardinal the *renal veins.*

Unlike the hepatic portal system, the renal portal system is transitory in the evolution of the vertebrates. It is not present in the most primitive forms and has dropped out in the mammals.

Comparative Anatomy of Venous System. Bearing in mind the primitive pattern and the development of the two portal systems, let us now consider the comparative anatomy of the venous system.

AGNATHA. The venous system of the cyclostomes varies little from the primitive pattern described above. The subintestinal has lost its connection with the anal loop; together with the remnants

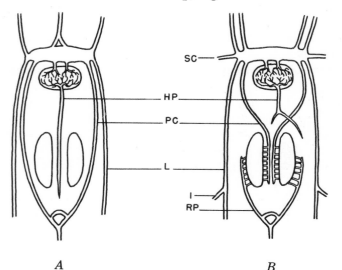

Fig. 12-6. *A,* diagram of venous system of adult agnathan; *B,* of fishes. SC, subclavian; I, iliac; HP, hepatic portal; PC, postcardinal; L, lateral; RP, renal portal.

of the vitelline veins, it breaks down into capillaries in the liver and thus forms a hepatic portal vein. The inferior jugulars unite to form a single median vessel. The anterior and posterior cardinals unite to enter the sinus as a single *common cardinal vein* (*duct of Cuvier*) (Fig. 12-6A).

Chondrichthyes and Osteichthyes. The Chondrichthyes and Osteichthyes show advances over the situation seen in the cyclostomes. It should be noted that with the development of limbs, new sets of veins also develop. The *subclavian veins* lead from the right and left anterior limbs into the paired ducts of Cuvier. The *iliac veins* lead from the posterior appendages into the lateral abdominal veins. The hepatic portal system is present.

The major advance made by the fishes over the cyclostomes is the development of a renal portal system. The subcardinals lose their connection with the anal loop, so that now blood coming anteriorly from the anal loop must of necessity pass through the renal portal veins to capillary beds in the kidneys and thence on through the subcardinals to the postcardinals and so through the common cardinals to the heart (Fig. 12-6B).

The venous system of the Dipnoi resembles that of the salamanders described below more closely than it does that of the other fishes.

Amphibia. As was true of the aortic arches, so also are two

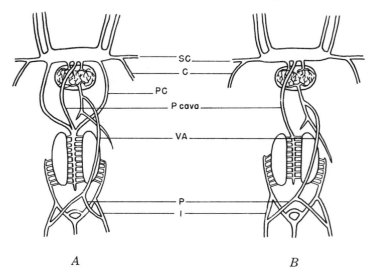

A
B

Fig. 12-7. *A*, diagram of venous system of salamander; *B*, of frog. C, cutaneous; P cava, post cava; VA, ventral abdominal; P, pelvic; other letters as in Fig. 12-6.

main patterns of the venous system found in the amphibians—
one in the Caudata and another in the Anura. The salamanders
show several important changes from the condition found in the
fishes. Pulmonary veins from the lungs enter the left atrium.
Cutaneous veins pass anteriorly along the lateral sides of the body
wall where they pick up blood that has been oxygenated by
cutaneous respiration. They enter the subclavian veins which join
the jugular and postcardinal veins to form the precavals. The
subcardinal veins are fused between the kidneys, but anterior to
the kidneys they diverge to join the postcardinals. A new vessel,
the *postcava,* passes posteriorly along the midline from the
posterior wall of the sinus venosus to join the subcardinals at the
point where they diverge anterior to the kidneys. Hence, once
blood has passed through the renal portal veins into the kidneys,
it has three possible pathways to the heart: it may flow through
the median postcava or through the right or the left postcardinal.

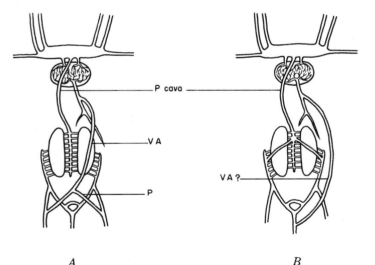

P cava

V A

P

VA ?

A

B

Fig. 12-8. *A,* diagram of venous system of reptile; *B,* of bird. The
ventral abdominal in the bird may not be truly homologous with
the abdominal of the lower tetrapods. Letters as in Fig. 12-7.

In the caudates the two lateral abdominal veins which were
present in the fishlike vertebrates have migrated medially and
ventrally and fused for most of their distance along the mid-

ventral line to form a new vessel, the *anterior abdominal* (or *ventral abdominal*) *vein.* This vessel now enters the hepatic portal vein instead of the sinus venosus. Posteriorly, where the two lateral abdominals have not fused along the midline, the paired portions are now known as the *pelvic veins.* They connect the iliacs with the anterior abdominal. The iliacs form connections with the renal portal veins so that blood from the hind limbs passes either through the kidneys or through the liver (Fig. 12-7A).

The venous system of the frogs is similar to that of the salamanders except in one major respect. In the frogs, the right and left postcardinals have disintegrated so that blood coming from the kidneys has but one passageway to the heart, that is, through the median postcaval vein. The precavae are formed from the jugular and subclavian veins (Fig. 12-7B).

REPTILIA. The pattern in the reptiles is very much like that in the frogs, except that since there is no cutaneous respiration through the dry, scaly reptilian skin, the cutaneous vessels present in the amphibians have dropped out. (See Fig. 12-8A, p. 147.)

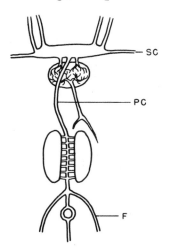

FIG. 12-9. Diagram of venous system of mammal. F, femoral vein; SC, subclavian; PC, postcardinal.

AVES. In birds, blood passing from the "renal portal" vein to the postcava may now bypass the capillary beds of the kidney. A direct venous pathway has developed within the kidney between the "renal portal" and the postcava. Hence, the birds can hardly be said to have a true renal portal system, since most of the blood goes directly through a vein from the old renal portal into the postcava. However, some capillary connections may persist. Instead of the paired pelvics and median ventral abdominal found in the reptiles, the birds have a median vessel, known either as the *coccygeomesenteric, inferior mesenteric,* or *caudal mesenteric,* which leads from the caudal vein into the hepatic portal system. There is some question as to whether this vessel is really homologous with the anterior abdominal of the amphibians and reptiles (Fig. 12-8B, p. 147).

MAMMALIA. The venous pattern of the mammals has advanced beyond that of the birds in that the renal portal system has completely disappeared. All blood coming into the kidney is now arterial blood. The blood passes directly from the caudal vein through the postcava and thence to the heart. Furthermore, the old anterior abdominal vein of the reptiles has disappeared so that now all blood from the limbs and tail region must pass through the postcava (Fig. 12-9).

LYMPHATIC SYSTEM

As the blood-vascular system transports blood, so the lymphatic system transports lymph. Lymph consists of tissue fluid (the fluid surrounding the cells of the body) that has made its way into the lymph vessels. The lymphatic system is made up of *lymph capillaries, lymph vessels, sinuses, lymph hearts,* and *lymph nodes.*

Structure of the Lymphatic System. The lymphatic vessels originate in mesenchyme quite independently of the blood-vascular system. The connections between the venous system and the lymphatic system are secondary developments.

The tubular units of the lymphatic system are the lymph capillaries, tiny vessels with their walls made up of squamous endothelium. These lymph capillaries terminate blindly at their free ends. Proximally, they unite to form larger vessels which in turn unite to form vessels of still greater caliber. These larger lymphatic vessels, like small arteries, are made up of three layers—a tunica externa, tunica media, and tunica interna—although these layers are not so distinct as they are in blood vessels. The largest of the lymphatic vessels finally open into the blood-vascular system by entering veins, usually near the heart. The lymphatic vessels, like veins, have valves to prevent the backward flow of lymph.

Associated with the lymph vessels there may be lymph nodes and lymph hearts. Lymph nodes are masses of lymphatic tissue composed of connective tissue fibers enclosing a large number of cells, namely the lymphocytes and macrophages. The lymph vessels ramify their way through these nodes. In addition to lymph nodes, lymph hearts may be present; these are pulsating enlargements of the lymphatic vessels which have contractile muscles in their walls. If lymph hearts are present, they are generally situated near the point where the lymphatic system connects with the venous system.

Comparative Anatomy of Lymphatic System. Not a great deal is known about the comparative anatomy of the lymphatic system, particularly in the lower vertebrates, since the delicate nature and small size of the lymphatic vessels make study of these structures extremely difficult. Most of the work done in this field has been concerned with the birds and mammals.

Osteichthyes. In general, the lymphatic system seems to be extensively developed in the fishes. There are a number of connections between the lymphatic and venous systems and these connections may occur in the posterior and middle part of the body as well as the anterior part. Although most fishes lack lymph hearts, the Old World catfish, *Silurus,* has two lymph hearts in the tail region. The eel has a single lymph heart in the tail, and lymph hearts have been described for a few other forms near the points of junction between the lymphatic vessels and the veins. No lymph nodes in the fishes have been reported.

Amphibia. The caudate amphibians have two sets of lymphatic vessels: a set of superficial vessels beneath the skin carry lymph to the cutaneous and postcardinal veins; and a set of deeper vessels along each side of the dorsal aorta enter the subclavian veins. The salamanders have numerous lymph hearts, as many as twenty having been described for the superficial vessels alone. In the adult frogs and toads large lymph sacs or lymph spaces occur beneath the skin. Most of the lymph is pumped toward the heart by two pairs of lymph hearts. The first pair lies behind the third vertebra and pumps lymph into the vertebral vein. The posterior, or second, pair of lymph hearts lies near the end of the urostyle and pumps blood into the iliac veins. Lymph hearts are more numerous in the larval and tadpole stages. Some of the apode amphibians have been reported to have as many as two hundred lymph hearts.

Reptilia. The lymphatic system of reptiles is well developed. The lymphatic vessels of the snakes are exceptionally large and numerous. The reptiles have only a single pair of lymph hearts, which pump lymph into the iliac veins.

Aves. The lymphatic channels of the birds empty ultimately into the precaval veins. No adult birds are known to have lymph hearts, although transitory lymph hearts may be observed in the pelvic region during embryonic development.

Mammalia. Most of the lymph vessels of the mammals come together to form a large *thoracic duct* which enters the venous system by means of the left subclavian vein. In addition to this main group of vessels, a smaller group on the right side of the head and neck join to form the *right lymphatic duct* which enters the right subclavian vein. No lymph hearts have been described for any adult mammal. On the other hand, lymph nodes are very abundant, particularly in the superficial regions of the head and neck, in the axilla and groin, and in the mesentery associated with the intestine. They seem to function primarily in preventing the invasion of the body by bacteria. The phagocytic action of the macrophages already mentioned (p. 150) is primarily responsible for this type of body protection.

13

Nervous System

The nervous system is concerned with the co-ordination and control of bodily activities and with adjustment of the animal to changes in the environment by the transmission of impulses from the sense organs to the effectors (muscles and glands). The nervous system of the vertebrate body is derived entirely from ectodermal tissue. Most of it develops from the embryonic neural tube and neural crests, but it may in part develop from sensory placodes which form as thickenings of the superficial ectoderm.

STRUCTURE OF NERVOUS SYSTEM

The functional unit of the nervous system is the nerve cell or *neuron.* This is made up of at least three parts: a *cell body;* the *axon,* a process carrying impulses away from the cell body; and the *dendrites,* one or more processes carrying impulses toward the cell body.[4]

There are three types of neurons: *sensory,* or *afferent,* neurons which carry impulses from the sensory receptors toward the central nervous system; *motor,* or *efferent,* neurons which carry impulses from the central nervous system to the muscles and glands; and *association* neurons which transmit impulses between the sensory and motor neurons and between parts of the central nervous system.

The nerves we see when we dissect an animal are made of

[4] Sometimes a dendrite is defined as a short, highly branched process that does not extend far from the cell body while an axon is defined as a long process with branching largely confined to its end. However, since the afferent process of a sensory neuron may also be long and relatively unbranched, it seems better to define the processes on a functional rather than on a structural basis.

bundles of nerve processes (*nerve fibers*). Bundles of nerve fibers within the brain or spinal cord are known as *nerve* or *fiber tracts*. Fiber tracts that connect similar regions on opposite sides of the central nervous system are called *commissures*. Groups of nerve cell bodies lying outside the brain and spinal cord are called *ganglia* (sing., *ganglion*), while such groups within the brain or cord are called *nuclei*. A neuron is gray in color, but frequently a fiber is covered by a white sheath, the *myelin sheath*. Nervous tissue made up of cell bodies and of unmyelinated fibers is known as *gray matter*. Tissue made up of myelinated (*medullated*) fibers is yellowish white in color and is known as *white matter*. In some regions, gray and white matter are intermingled to some extent; such an arrangement is known as a *reticular formation*.

Besides the neurons, two other types of cells are involved in the formation of the nervous system: *neuroglia cells* and *ependymal cells*. The neuroglia cells are ectodermal in origin and lie dispersed among the neurons. There is no true connective tissue present in the nervous system; instead, support and protection are provided for the neurons by the several types of neuroglia cells. The ependymal cells are also ectodermal in origin. They are nonnervous supporting cells which line the cavities of the brain and spinal cord. They are often ciliated.

For purposes of study, it is convenient to divide the nervous system into two parts: the *central nervous system* is composed of the brain and the spinal cord; the *peripheral nervous system* is composed of the nerves and ganglia which are connected with the central nervous system but lie outside it. The *autonomic nervous system*, usually considered separately, is that part of the peripheral nervous system that transmits impulses to structures not under voluntary control (the smooth muscles, heart, and glands).

CENTRAL NERVOUS SYSTEM

The neural plate of the developing embryo at first consists of a single layer of epithelial cells. By the time the neural plate has folded over to form the neural tube, its walls have become thickened and comprise several layers. Two types of cells develop from these original epithelial cells of the neural plate: *neuroblasts* and *spongioblasts*. The neuroblasts subsequently give rise to neurons, while the spongioblasts give rise to ependymal and neuroglial elements. After the tube is formed, its walls soon differentiate into three rather definite layers: an innermost *epithelial layer* of ependymal cells; a middle, nucleated, nervous *mantle layer;* and an outermost, fibrous, *marginal layer* made up of neuroglial elements. It is this neural tube that develops into the brain and spinal cord.

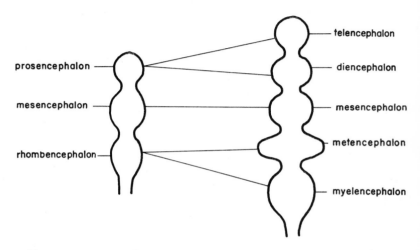

prosencephalon

mesencephalon

rhombencephalon

telencephalon

diencephalon

mesencephalon

metencephalon

myelencephalon

FIG. 13-1. Diagram showing the differentiation of the anterior end of the neural tube into the divisions of the brain.

The Brain. The brain of the developing embryo first becomes apparent as an enlargement of the anterior end of the neural tube. As the brain enlarges, it differentiates into three portions: a *forebrain,* or *prosencephalon;* a *midbrain,* or *mesencephalon;* and a *hindbrain,* or *rhombencephalon.* Associated with the enlargement of these three portions of the brain there is of necessity a folding which takes place primarily at three points: between the spinal cord and hindbrain, the *cervical flexure;* between the hindbrain and midbrain, the *pontine flexure;* and between the midbrain and forebrain, the *cephalic flexure.*

Divisions of the Brain. With further growth and differentiation, the parts of the brain subdivide. The prosencephalon gives rise to two parts: the anterior portion is the *telencephalon,* destined ultimately to form the *cerebral hemispheres* of the higher vertebrates; and the posterior part is the *diencephalon,* more familiarly known as the *'tween brain.* The mesencephalon remains more or less undifferentiated so far as dividing into anterior and posterior sections is concerned. The hindbrain or rhombencephalon divides into an anterior portion, the *metencephalon,* which gives rise to the *cerebellum,* and a posterior portion, the *myelencephalon* or *medulla oblongata.* (The development of the parts of the brain is summarized in Fig. 13-1.)

We shall consider these parts separately, beginning posteriorly with the myelencephalon (the best developed part of the brain in the cyclostomes), and progressing anteriorly to the telencephalon which reaches its greatest development in the mammals.

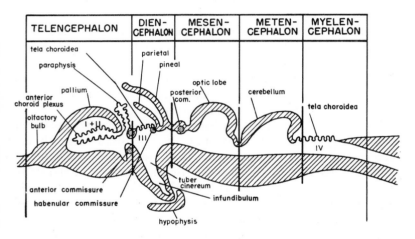

Fɪɢ. 13-2. Diagrammatic sagittal section of a shark brain, showing its divisions and structures. (From Adams and Eddy, *Comparative Anatomy,* John Wiley & Sons, 1949, by permission.)

Mʏᴇʟᴇɴᴄᴇᴘʜᴀʟᴏɴ. The myelencephalon (medulla oblongata) is well developed in all the vertebrates. Its floor and walls are fairly thick, but its roof is quite thin, being made up of a single layer of ependymal cells from the brain itself and a pia layer from the surrounding membrane (see under meninges, p. 178). These two fuse to form a single coat, the *tela choroidea,* which forms the roof of the myelencephalon. The cavity of the myelencephalon is the *fourth ventricle* of the brain. Where the tela choroidea folds into the fourth ventricle, it is known as the *posterior choroid plexus.* The roots of cranial nerves V through X in the anamniotes and V through XII in the amniotes stem from the myelencephalon. The myelencephalon serves as a control center for the regulation of such functions as heartbeat, respiration, and metabolism.

METENCEPHALON. The metencephalon, like the myelencephalon, has thick walls and a thick floor, but in addition its roof becomes thickened to form the cerebellum. The cerebellum is the center of proprioception, the so-called muscle sense. In the cortex, or outer layer, of the cerebellum are the extremely complexly branched *Purkinje cells* which are characteristic of the structure and are believed to play an important part in the correlation of nerve impulses with muscular movements of an equilibratory nature.

MESENCEPHALON. The mesencephalon has a fairly thick floor and thick walls; lateral outgrowths from it form the *optic lobes.* The optic lobes may each be divided by a *transverse fissure.* When they are not so divided, they are known as the *corpora bigemina;* when they are divided, so that they form four prominences, they are known as the *corpora quadrigemina.*

The anterior roof of the mesencephalon contains the *posterior commissure,* fiber tracts connecting the two sides of the brain. The cavity of the mesencephalon is the *aqueduct of Sylvius* or *cerebral aqueduct.* It connects the fourth ventricle of the brain within the myelencephalon with the third ventricle which lies in the more anterior diencephalon. The roots of the third and fourth cranial nerves originate in the mesencephalon.

DIENCEPHALON. The diencephalon is an extremely complex portion of the brain. The cavity of the diencephalon is the *third ventricle.* The anterior part of its roof, like the roof of the myelencephalon, is thin, composed only of ependymal and pia elements which form a tela choroidea. The tela choroidea may fold into the ventricle to form the *anterior choroid plexus* which may extend into the first and second ventricles of the telencephalon. Folds of the tela choroidea which extend anteriorly to overlap the telencephalon are known as the *paraphysis.*

Posterior to the tela choroidea, the roof of the diencephalon is thicker and is known as the *epithalamus.* From it two outgrowths may develop: an anterior *parietal body;* and a more posterior *pineal body,* also known as the *epiphysis.* The parietal body is the structure that gives rise to the third eye of *Sphenodon* and certain lizards. It is absent in many vertebrates. The function of the pineal body is somewhat conjectural. There is some evidence that it is glandular in nature, although whether it is an actual endocrine gland or merely a vestigial structure is still a moot question. Just in front of the pineal body lie the *habenular bodies,* nuclei through which olfactory stimuli pass. They are connected by the *habenular commissure.*

The lateral walls of the diencephalon are thickened to form the *thalamus* and they may meet on the midline in the *soft commissure.* The floor of the diencephalon is known as the *hypothalamus.* It is a center of control for involuntary visceral functions of the body. From the floor of the hypothalamus there develops an *infundibulum* which grows ventrally and fuses with Rathke's pouch from the roof of the stomodaeum to give rise to the *pituitary body* or *hypophysis.*

The roots of the second cranial nerves originate from the diencephalon.

TELENCEPHALON. The telecephalon is the most anterior portion of the brain. The *anterior commissure* of the brain is formed on the posterior floor of the telencephalon. The most anterior portion of the telencephalon gives rise to the *olfactory lobes.* Behind the olfactory lobes lie the cerebral hemispheres, which contain the *first* (right) and *second* (left) *ventricles.* The floor of the hemispheres is thickened to form the *corpus striatum.* The remaining part of the hemispheres, forming the roof of the ventricles, is the *pallium* which ultimately gives rise to the cerebral cortex of the higher vertebrates. As mentioned before, the tela choroidea of the diencephalon folds over the telencephalon to form the paraphysis; the anterior choroid plexus is located in the region of the juncture of the first and second ventricles with the third ventricle.

The roots of the cranial nerves O and I originate in the telencephalon.

Comparative Anatomy of the Vertebrate Brain. Differences in the brains of the various classes of vertebrates result from differences in the degree of development of the structures outlined above.

AGNATHA. In the cyclostomes the myelencephalon is the only part of the brain that is really well developed. In many ways it is fairly typical, but the posterior choroid plexus of the lampreys, instead of folding into the cavity of the myelencephalon, everts outward as a saclike structure. Large neurons present in the myelencephalon of the cyclostomes have axons that go all the way into the tail and presumably have some function in swimming. The metencephalon, particularly the cerebellar part, is very poorly developed. The mesencephalon, like the bulk of the brain in the cyclostomes, is poorly developed and the optic lobes form simple corpora bigemina. The epithalamus gives rise to both parietal and pineal bodies, but the pineal body of the cyclostomes differs from that of all other vertebrates in that it forms an eyelike structure. The telencephalon is extremely poorly developed and, as in all fishlike vertebrates, functions only in the transmission of olfactory impulses. The corpus striatum, or bottom portion, is very insignificant and the roof, or pallium, is so thin that it is scarcely visible.

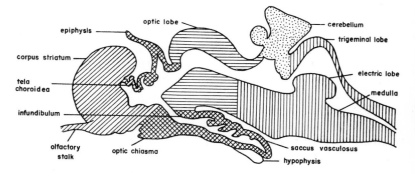

Fig. 13-3. Diagrammatic sagittal section of the brain of a ray. (From Walter and Sayles, *Biology of the Vertebrates*, Macmillan, 1949, by permission.)

CHONDRICHTHYES. The myelencephalon of the Chondrichthyes, as of all vertebrates, is well developed. The cartilaginous fishes resemble the cyclostomes in that large neurons located in the myelencephalon have axons that terminate in the muscular tail and presumably are utilized in swimming. The cerebellum of the elasmobranchs is usually well developed and may have a lobed appearance. The metencephalon in some of the cartilaginous fishes gives rise to irregular projections, the *restiform bodies*, which probably function in equilibration. The mesencephalon forms simple corpora bigemina. The diencephalon has both parietal and pineal bodies growing out from the epithalamus. The infundibulum gives rise to lateral *inferior lobes* and a terminal, thin-walled *saccus vasculosus;* the function of these structures is unknown. The telencephalon of the Chondrichthyes has a fairly thick corpus striatum; the pallium is moderately thick, but has no true nervous tissue in it (Figs. 13-2 and 13-3).

OSTEICHTHYES. The myelencephalon of the bony fishes, like that of the preceding forms, contains large neurons with axons that terminate in the tail. The myelencephalon of many fishes is further differentiated by the presence of large *vagal lobes* which function as centers of taste. The cerebellum of the metencephalon is poorly developed in the sluggish fishes, better developed in the more active ones. Some bony fishes, like some elasmobranchs, have restiform bodies developed from the metencephalon which function in equilibration. The mesencephalon of the fishes gives rise to simple corpora bigemina as optic lobes. Many fishes develop both parietal and pineal bodies as outgrowths of the epithalamus. Inferior lobes and a saccus vasculosus develop from the infundibulum. The hemispheres of the telencephalon are small and the roof or pallium is very thin (Fig. 13-4).

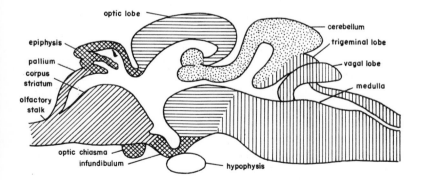

FIG. 13-4. Diagrammatic sagittal section through the brain of a bony fish. (From Walter and Sayles, *Biology of the Vertebrates*, Macmillan, 1949, by permission.)

AMPHIBIA. In amphibians, as in all tetrapods, the vagal lobes so prominent in the fishes are no longer present. The large neurons of the myelencephalon with axons going to the tail are still present in the Caudata, although they are lacking in the anurans. So far as the metencephalon is concerned, the cerebellum is poorly developed. The optic lobes from the roof of the mesencephalon form simple corpora bigemina. The parietal and pineal bodies extending from the roof of the diencephalon fuse into a single structure. The hypothalamus, like that of the fishes, gives rise to inferior lobes and a saccus vasculosus. In the amphibians for the first time the roof of the telencephalon, the pallium, divides into a median *archipallium* and lateral *paleopallium;* nevertheless, the telencephalon of the amphibians is still purely olfactory in function (Fig. 13-5).

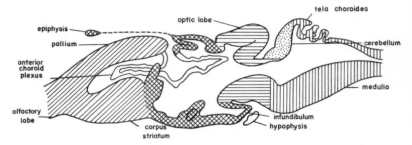

FIG. 13-5. Diagrammatic sagittal section through the brain of an amphibian. (From Walter and Sayles, *Biology of the Vertebrates,* Macmillan, 1949, by permission.)

REPTILIA. The reptiles, forming as they do the first of the series of amniotes, are likewise the first vertebrates to have the eleventh and twelfth cranial nerves. These nerves arise from the myelencephalon together with the roots of cranial nerves V to X mentioned earlier (see p. 156). The metencephalon is still fairly poorly developed in reptiles. The cerebellum is usually simple; it is best developed in the swimmers, particularly in the crocodilians in which small, lateral, *floccular lobes* extend from it. These seem to correspond to the restiform bodies of the fishes. The optic lobes of snakes are divided by a transverse fissure into four prominences, the corpora quadrigemina. Many reptiles have well developed parietal and pineal bodies, and in some reptiles for the first time the walls of the diencephalon become thickened and meet in the midline to form a soft commissure.

It is in the telencephalon that we find the most striking development of the reptilian brain. The cerebral hemispheres are larger than in the amphibians, and in certain reptiles a new area, the *neopallium,* appears anteriorly between the archipallium and the paleopallium. In the crocodilians, nerve cells migrate into the neopallium and become arranged along its outer surface, thus forming a true *cerebral cortex* for the first time. The cerebral cortex of the crocodilians has a smooth surface (Fig. 13-6).

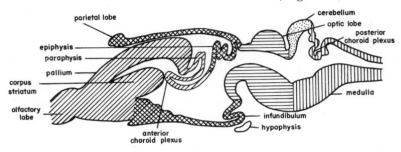

FIG. 13-6. Diagrammatic sagittal section through the brain of a reptile. (From Walter and Sayles, *Biology of the Vertebrates,* Macmillan, 1949, by permission.)

Aves. The myelencephalon of the birds, like that of the reptiles, serves as a place of origin of cranial nerves V through XII. The cerebellum is extremely large and covers the tela choroidea posteriorly. Along its median portion an area, the *vermis,* develops; it is vaguely divided into anterior, middle, and posterior

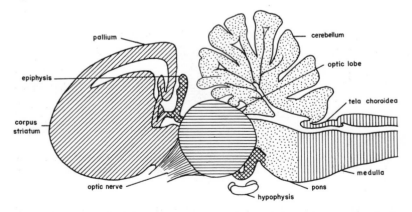

FIG. 13-7. Diagrammatic sagittal section through the brain of a bird. (From Walter and Sayles, *Biology of the Vertebrates,* Macmillan, 1949, by permission.)

portions. The vermis is bounded on the sides by well developed floccular lobes. Furthermore, some birds show for the first time a true *pons*, a thickening of the floor of the cerebellum formed by fiber tracts, between the cerebellum and the cerebral lobes. The fiber tracts of the pons from each side cross under the base of the cerebellum.

The optic lobes of birds, while large, are simple corpora bigemina as in all forms heretofore mentioned except the snakes. The parietal body has finally disappeared and only the pineal body remains as an outgrowth from the roof of the diencephalon. The olfactory lobes of the telencephalon are rudimentary, but the telencephalon is extremely large because of the great development of the corpus striatum. The archipallium, paleopallium, and neopallium are present, but the cerebral cortex is poorly developed (Fig. 13-7).

MAMMALIA. The myelencephalon of the mammals resembles that of the birds and reptiles. The mammals have a well developed cerebellum with the vermis sharply divided into three portions. The entire structure is thrown into folds (*gyri*) separated by grooves (*sulci*) whereby the surface area is increased. There

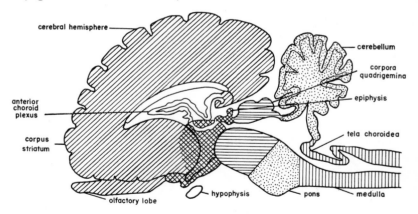

FIG. 13-8. Diagrammatic sagittal section through the brain of a mammal. (From Walter and Sayles, *Biology of the Vertebrates*, Macmillan, 1949, by permission.)

is a well developed pons in the mammalian mesencephalon. As in snakes, the optic lobes form well developed corpora quadrigemina. The parietal body is absent. The thick walls of the diencephalon meet along the midline to form a soft commissure. It is in the telencephalon that the greatest step has been made in the evolution of the mammalian brain. The cortex of the cerebral hemispheres is extremely well developed and has become heavily folded with numerous gyri and sulci (Fig. 13-8).

The Spinal Cord. The spinal cord, sometimes known as the *myelon,* does not undergo the extensive differentiation that the anterior portion of the embryonic neural tube, the brain, undergoes. In most vertebrates, it is a more or less cylindrical, simple tube, wide at the anterior end where it is continuous with the myelencephalon and usually tapering at the posterior end to a fine, threadlike structure, the *filum terminale.* In higher forms, the cord is incompletely divided into right and left halves by a *ventral fissure* and a *dorsal septum* which extends ventrally from a slight median depression, the *sulcus,* on the dorsal surface.

Comparative Anatomy of the Spinal Cord. The most important evolutionary change shown in the spinal cord of the various classes of vertebrates is in the arrangement of the white matter comprising the myelinated fibers and of the gray matter comprising the nerve cell bodies and unmyelinated fibers.

AGNATHA. Since the central canal of the spinal cord of amphioxus is slit-shaped and has not yet closed over at the top, the cyclostomes are the first of the chordates to show a truly tubular cord. In the cyclostomes, the cord is rather uniform in diameter throughout its length and is somewhat flattened dorsoventrally. Neither the dorsal septum nor the ventral fissure have yet made their appearance. There is no sharp differentiation between gray and white matter in the cord.

CHONDRICHTHYES AND OSTEICHTHYES. The cord of the fishes is more rounded than that of the cyclostomes and a dorsal fissure is usually present, although the ventral fissure has not yet developed. The gray matter is arranged more or less in the form of a triangle with the apex pointing dorsally, and paired ventral columns of gray matter are also present. The white matter surrounds the gray matter. In a great majority of fishes, the cord tapers gradually to the end of the tail, but in some it is foreshortened and does not reach to the end of the vertebral column. The marine sunfish, for example, a fish which may reach a length of about 250 cm., has a cord less than 1.8 cm. in length.

AMPHIBIA. In the amphibians, the dorsal sulcus is usually present and a ventral fissure appears for the first time. The gray matter shows the beginning of the typical H-shaped arrangement seen in the higher vertebrates, and the fiber tracts of white matter are more clearly indicated than in the non-tetrapods. The cord of the salamanders usually extends to the posterior end of the vertebral column. In the frogs, however, the cord is shortened so that the posterior end of the neural canal of the vertebral column is occupied simply by a slender filum terminale plus the roots of spinal nerves that come off from the cord and continue to the posterior end of the vertebral column before they make their exit between the vertebrae. This bundle of roots of spinal nerves in the posterior part of the vertebral column of an animal with a foreshortened spinal cord is known as the *cauda equina* ("horse's tail"). The cervical and lumbar enlargements so characteristic of the spinal cord of the tetrapods first appear in the amphibians. These result from the increase in the number of neurons required for the innervation of the more complex tetrapod limbs.

REPTILIA. Among the reptiles, the spinal cord extends the full length of the vertebral column. Cervical and lumbar enlargements are present in all reptiles except the snakes and limbless lizards. The H-shaped arrangement of gray matter in the cord is typical of that found in the other amniotes. The dorsal sulcus and ventral fissure are present.

AVES. The spinal cord of the birds is essentially reptilian in character except for the fact that an elliptical space, the *sinus rhomboidalis,* is present on the dorsal side of the lumbar enlargement.

MAMMALIA. In a few mammals the spinal cord extends to the tip of the vertebral column, but in most of them it is shorter than the column and a well developed cauda equina is present. As in all of the amniotes, a dorsal sulcus and a ventral fissure are present. The latter is particularly prominent in the mammals.

PERIPHERAL NERVOUS SYSTEM

In order fully to understand the structure and functioning of the peripheral nervous system it is necessary to have an understanding of the four basic types of nerve fibers involved. Nerve fibers in the peripheral nervous system may be either *sensory* (*afferent*), carrying impulses into the central nervous system, or *motor* (*efferent*), carrying impulses to effectors throughout the body. The types of fibers are further subdivided depending on whether they are associated with somatic structures (such as the muscles and skin) or with purely visceral structures. Hence, there are four recognizable types of fibers that may occur in nerves: *somatic sensory, visceral sensory, visceral motor,* and *somatic motor.*

The nerves, with their associated ganglia, that make up the peripheral nervous system, may be either spinal nerves, arising from the spinal cord, or cranial nerves, arising from the brain.

Spinal Nerves. The spinal nerves are paired, metameric structures which, except in the lampreys, arise from the cord by two roots. The dorsal root bears a swelling, the *dorsal root ganglion,* composed of the cell bodies of the *sensory* neurons. The ventral root carries only *motor* fibers whose cell bodies are housed in the spinal cord. Shortly beyond the point where the roots fuse to form the spinal nerve, the nerve itself typically divides into three branches: a *dorsal ramus,* a *ventral ramus,* and a *ramus communicans* (or *visceral ramus*). Each of these branches carries both motor and sensory fibers. In general, the dorsal ramus innervates the epaxial muscles and associated structures; the ventral ramus innervates the hypaxial muscles and associated structures; and the ramus communicans innervates the viscera. In the region of the limbs, the ventral rami of several spinal nerves anastomose to form a complex network or *plexus.*

Comparative Anatomy of Spinal Nerves. The major evolutionary change shown by the spinal nerves is in the composition of the dorsal root. Primitively it comprises both sensory and motor fibers, but in amniotes the motor fibers have shifted to the ventral root so that the dorsal root is purely sensory.

AGNATHA. Among the lampreys, the dorsal and ventral roots do not join to form a single nerve; instead there are dorsal and ventral nerves which alternate with each other. The dorsal nerve joins the dorsal portion of the cord and carries somatic sensory, visceral sensory, and visceral motor fibers. The ventral nerve exits from the more ventral portion of the cord and carries only somatic motor fibers. Among the myxinoids, the two roots usually join except in the tail region.

CHONDRICHTHYES AND OSTEICHTHYES. The fishes have more or

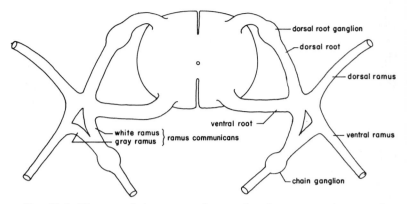

Fig. 13-9. Diagram of the roots and rami of a thoracic spinal nerve of a mammal. The ramus communicans is typically divided into a gray ramus and a white ramus.

less typical spinal nerves, formed by the union of dorsal and ventral roots. The dorsal root carries both somatic and visceral sensory fibers, as well as visceral motor elements. The ventral root carries somatic motor and visceral motor elements. Plexuses are present. The dorsal roots of some of the anterior spinal nerves have disappeared so that these nerves are purely motor. They are called *spino-occipital* nerves.

AMPHIBIA. The spinal nerves of the amphibians are essentially the same as those of the fishes, with the dorsal root still containing some visceral motor elements. A well developed *brachial plexus* (innervating the fore limb) and a *lumbosacral plexus* (innervating the hind limb) are usually present.

REPTILIA. In the reptiles for the first time all the visceral motor elements have become associated with the ventral root so that the dorsal root is entirely sensory. This is a characteristic of the amniotes, as is the presence of the eleventh and twelfth cranial nerves. Spino-occipital nerves are no longer present in the amniotes since their fibers are now all involved in the formation of these two cranial nerves. Well developed plexuses are present in the reptiles with limbs. Some snakes and the legless lizards have a distinct, though poorly developed, lumbosacral plexus, indicating that these animals evolved from forms with limbs.

AVES AND MAMMALIA. In both birds and mammals the dorsal root of the spinal nerve is entirely sensory, carrying somatic sen-

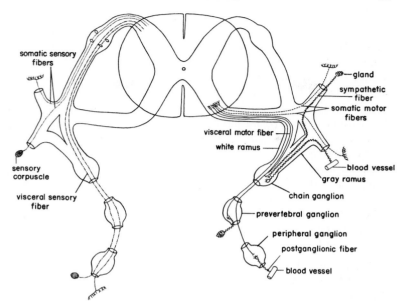

Fig. 13-10. Diagram showing the types of fibers in the roots and rami of a thoracic spinal nerve of a mammal. Only motor fibers are shown on the right and only sensory fibers on the left. (Redrawn from Weichert, *Elements of Chordate Anatomy*, McGraw-Hill, 1953, by permission.)

sory and visceral sensory elements. The ventral root is entirely motor, carrying visceral motor and somatic motor elements. (The typical structure of a thoracic spinal nerve of a bird or a mammal is shown in Fig. 13-10.)

Cranial Nerves. Cranial nerves are those peripheral nerves that form connections with the brain. It is sometimes possible to homologize the parts of a cranial nerve with the parts of a spinal nerve. For example, the hypoglossal or twelfth cranial nerve, when first formed embryonically, has two roots and a dorsal root ganglion. In development both the dorsal root and dorsal root ganglion disappear, leaving a purely motor nerve. This nerve might be homologous with the hypobranchial nerve which is formed from branches of the spino-occipital nerves in the lower vertebrates. Some of the cranial nerves carry both sensory and motor fibers and are said to be "mixed." However, if they do indeed have both dorsal and ventral roots, these roots unite before the nerves emerge from the medulla.

While it is customary to speak of cranial nerves as being either motor or sensory or mixed, it should be pointed out that such strict classification must be recognized as somewhat exaggerated. Such purely motor nerves as the oculomotor do in fact have a few sensory fibers, for the proprioceptive stimuli coming from eye muscles pass along this nerve on their way to the brain. If, however, we ignore proprioceptors, we can distinguish the three fundamental types of cranial nerves: purely sensory, purely motor, and mixed. Nerves with sensory fibers may have ganglia lying outside the brain.

Descriptions of Cranial Nerves. The cranial nerves are very similar in all the vertebrates. They are designated by Roman numerals, which are given in parentheses after the names of the nerves described below. The most anterior nerve, which was discovered after the numerals had been assigned to the others, is designated by O.

TERMINAL NERVE (O). The terminal nerve leaves the anterior ventral portion of the cerebral hemisphere and passes anteriorly. This nerve is best developed in the elasmobranch fishes. In the amphibians, reptiles, and mammals, it is apparently associated with Jacobson's organ. It is purely sensory in function.

OLFACTORY NERVE (I). This nerve also originates from the telencephalon. In vertebrates that have the olfactory lobe drawn out into a bulb and tract, the olfactory tract is sometimes mistaken for the nerve proper. Actually, the nerve consists of many separate fibers running from the bulb into the olfactory epithelium. It also sends a branch to Jacobson's organ in those animals that have this structure. It is a purely sensory nerve.

OPTIC NERVE (II). This structure is not really a nerve but is actually a tract of the brain, since it passes from one portion of the brain, the *optic cup,* to another, the mesencephalon. However, it is usually included with the cranial nerves. It consists of nerve fibers of neurons whose cell bodies are in the retina of the eye. The optic nerves cross beneath the diencephalon to form the *optic chiasma.* This chiasma lies within the brain of the cyclostomes, but in all the higher vertebrates it is on the surface below the diencephalon. Complete crossing of all the fibers occurs in the chiasma of all vertebrates except those mammals that have binocular vision. In these forms, about half of the fibers of each tract stay on the same side of the brain as the eye from which they come. The optic nerve is sensory in function.

OCULOMOTOR NERVE (III). This purely motor nerve (excepting proprioceptors) supplies the muscles derived from the myotome of the first, or premandibular, pro-otic somite. The nerve leaves the ventral side of the mesencephalon and passes, in all vertebrates except the cyclostomes, to the inferior oblique, superior rectus, inferior rectus, and internal rectus eye muscles. In the lamprey it passes only to the superior rectus, internal rectus, and inferior oblique, the inferior rectus being supplied by the abducens nerve.

TROCHLEAR NERVE (IV). This nerve passes from the mesencephalon to the superior oblique eye muscle, which is derived from the mandibular, or second, pro-otic somite. Like the oculomotor, it is a somatic motor nerve, but carries a few proprioceptive fibers.

TRIGEMINAL NERVE (V). This large nerve originates from the anterior end of the myelencephalon and is essentially the nerve of the mandibular arch. It is characteristically divided into three main branches: the *ophthalmic,* the *maxillary,* and the *mandibular.* The ophthalmic branch passes to the region of the nose and of the snout in animals that have a nose or snout, and to parts of the face in others; the maxillary branch typically passes to the upper jaw and its associated structures; the mandibular branch typically passes to the lower jaw and associated structures. The nerve bears a large *Gasserian ganglion* near its point of origin. The ophthalmic and maxillary branches carry only somatic sensory fibers; the mandibular carries both somatic sensory and visceral motor fibers.

ABDUCENS NERVE (VI). This small nerve arises from the ventral part of the myelencephalon near its anterior end and passes to the external rectus eye muscle, which is derived from the third, or hyoid, pro-otic somite. Like the other nerves that go to the eye muscles, it is a somatic motor nerve, though it carries a few proprioceptive fibers. In the lamprey, some fibers of this nerve innervate the inferior rectus muscle.

FACIAL NERVE (VII). This nerve arises from the myelencephalon and is basically the nerve of the second, or hyoid, arch. In the lower vertebrates, it has branches (*superficial ophthalmic* and *buccal*) which are distributed to the lateral line system, particularly the portion of the system around the head and face. Another main branch (*hyomandibular*) passes posteriorly to the structures associated with the hyoid arch. With the loss of the lateral line system in terrestrial vertebrates, the nerve passes primarily to structures on the side of the head and face, and to some extent to structures on the side of the neck. The taste buds of the mammalian tongue are partially supplied by this nerve. It is a mixed nerve and bears the *geniculate ganglion*.

Acoustic (Auditory) Nerve (VIII). The acoustic nerve passes from the side of the myelencephalon to the inner ear. In the higher forms, in which the ear serves as an organ both of hearing and of equilibration, there are two main branches. The *vestibular branch* carries impulses of equilibration and the *cochlear branch* carries auditory impulses. The lower forms, which lack auditory structures, also lack the cochlear branch. The acoustic is a purely somatic sensory nerve and bears an *acoustic ganglion* which is sometimes so closely associated with the geniculate ganglion of the previous nerve that it is difficult to distinguish between the two. When a cochlear branch is present, the acoustic ganglion is divided into *vestibular* and *spiral* (*cochlear*) *ganglia*.

Glossopharyngeal Nerve (IX). This nerve arises from the myelencephalon and seems to be the main nerve of the third visceral arch. In bony fishes its fibers pass to the structures associated with the first typical gill slit. It is a mixed nerve which carries both visceral sensory and visceral motor fibers, the sensory receiving sensations from the region of the third visceral arch and the motor controlling the activities of the muscles of this arch. A small sensory branch also goes to the pharynx where it supplies taste buds. This nerve bears a *petrosal ganglion* which is located close to the ganglion of the tenth cranial nerve (see below) and in the amphibians may actually fuse with it. The higher forms have also a small *superior ganglion*.

Vagus Nerve (X). The vagus nerve, which originates in the myelencephalon, is basically the nerve of the fourth and subsequent visceral arches. In the fishlike vertebrates, it innervates all the visceral arches posterior to the third and also has branches going to the pharynx and under the lateral line system nearly to the end of the tail. Since the amniotes have lost the gills, the branchial branches of the amniote vagus are lost for the most

TABLE 3

CRANIAL NERVES OF VERTEBRATES

Nerve		Somatic sensory	Visceral sensory	Visceral motor	Somatic motor	Ganglion
O.	Terminalis	X				
I.	Olfactory	X				
II.	Optic	X				
III.	Oculomotor			(X)	X	
IV.	Trochlear				X	
V.	Trigeminal	X		X		Gasserian
VI.	Abducens				X	
VII.	Facial	X	X	X		Geniculate
VIII.	Acoustic	X				Acoustic (Vestibular + spiral in tetrapods)
IX.	Glosso-pharyn-geal	(X)	X	X		Petrosal (+ Superior in amniotes)
X.	Vagus	(X)	X	X		Jugular (+ Lateralis in lower forms) (+ Nodosal in mammals)
XI.	Spinal Accessory			X	X	
XII.	Hypoglossal				X	

Proprioceptors not considered. Those in parentheses (X) indicate variable or negligible elements.

part; however, vagus fibers supply the larynx, trachea, lungs, and abdominal viscera in the anterior portion of the coelom. This nerve bears a *jugular ganglion* near its base; in lower forms a *lateralis ganglion* is also found, and in mammals a *nodosal ganglion* is present just distal to the jugular ganglion. This is a mixed nerve. Its visceral efferent fibers are important components of the autonomic system.

SPINAL ACCESSORY NERVE (XI). This nerve, which appears for the first time in the reptiles and is present in all amniotes, arises from the myelencephalon and passes to the region of the pharynx and larynx and to the sternocleidomastoid and trapezius muscles. It is a motor nerve, derived in part from the spino-occipital nerves of the anamniotes, and in part from visceral motor fibers of the vagus.

HYPOGLOSSAL NERVE (XII). This nerve, like the preceding one, is found only in amniotes; it is a purely somatic motor nerve, supplying intrinsic muscles of the tongue and other muscles below the tongue in the lower jaw. It is derived from spino-occipital nerves of the anamniotes. As might be expected, it is best developed in the mammals, since they have developed the greatest mobility of the tongue.

Table 3 (p. 171) summarizes certain information about the cranial nerves.

Comparative Anatomy of Cranial Nerves. Although the cranial nerves are very similar in all vertebrates, there is some variation that is worthy of comment.

AGNATHA. The terminal nerve O is absent. As mentioned above, the inferior rectus eye muscle of the cyclostomes is innervated by the abducens nerve instead of the oculomotor as it is in all the other vertebrates. Only the vestibular branch of the acoustic nerve exists, since these creatures lack auditory structures.

CHONDRICHTHYES AND OSTEICHTHYES. The cranial nerves of the Chondrichthyes and Osteichthyes are essentially alike. The ophthalmic branch of the fifth (trigeminal) nerve is divided into a *deep* and a *superficial ophthalmic.* As in the cyclostomes, the eighth has only a vestibular branch. The ninth (glossopharyngeal) nerve has a single ganglion, the petrosal. The tenth (vagus) nerve divides into a *lateralis branch* which innervates the lateral line and a *branchiovisceral branch* from which nerves pass to the posterior gill arches and to the anterior viscera.

AMPHIBIA. Among the tetrapods, the ophthalmic branch of the trigeminal forms a single trunk instead of dividing into deep and superficial branches as it does in the fishlike vertebrates. In the metamorphosed amphibians, the somatic sensory fibers of the seventh cranial nerve, which pass to the lateral line in the fishlike vertebrates, are reduced. With the development of the function of hearing by the tetrapods, the eighth cranial nerve becomes divided into two branches, namely, a vestibular branch and a cochlear branch. Also, among the metamorphosed amphibians, the lateralis and branchial branches of the tenth cranial nerve of the pisciform vertebrates have disappeared.

REPTILIA, AVES, AND MAMMALIA. The amniotes, like the amphibians, have a single ophthalmic trunk of the fifth cranial nerve and lack the lateralis and branchial branches of the tenth cranial nerve. The ninth cranial nerve of the reptiles, birds, and mammals now has two ganglia: the petrosal plus a small superior ganglion, which was not present in the lower vertebrates. The birds, like the cyclostomes, lack the terminal nerve (O). The eleventh and twelfth cranial nerves, the spinal accessory and hypoglossal, appear for the first time in the reptiles and persist throughout the amniotes.

AUTONOMIC NERVOUS SYSTEM

The autonomic nervous system is essentially a system of control of involuntary visceral functions; it is composed entirely of visceral motor elements. In other words, it is the *visceral efferent* system, controlling the action of smooth muscles and glands. The cell body of a somatic motor neuron is invariably located in the central nervous system and the fiber extends to the effector without interruption. On the other hand, efferent impulses of the autonomic nervous system must travel through two neurons. The cell body of the first neuron is located in the central nervous system; its axon, which is myelinated and is known as the *preganglionic fiber,* passes to a ganglion lying outside of the brain or spinal cord, where it forms a synapse with another neuron. The axon of this second neuron, which is unmyelinated and is known as the *postganglionic fiber,* then passes to the effector. The system is composed of these two types of fibers, together with the ganglia which serve as relay centers.

Certain cranial nerves carry efferent fibers to the branchial muscles. These are hypomeric muscles that have secondarily become voluntary in structure and function. Efferent fibers innervating them are considered visceral efferents, but not part of the autonomic system. All other visceral efferents are included in the autonomic system.

Since the autonomic system has been studied thoroughly only in the higher vertebrates, particularly the mammals, we will here simply give a description of its structure and functioning in the mammals and then conclude with a brief discussion of the system in the lower vertebrates.

Structure of the Autonomic System. There are two major divisions of the autonomic nervous system: the *sympathetic* and the *parasympathetic*. (The structural details of these divisions are shown in Figs. 13-11 and 13-12.) The sympathetic nervous system (sometimes called the *thoracolumbar outflow*) has preganglionic fibers coming from the thoracic and lumbar regions of the spinal column. The parasympathetic system (sometimes known as the *craniosacral outflow*) has preganglionic fibers coming from certain cranial and sacral nerves. Essentially the two systems, sympathetic and parasympathetic, are antagonistic to each other. The sympathetic system functions primarily to strengthen an animal's defenses by the expenditure of energy in some manner, while the parasympathetic system tends to bring the animal to a state of relaxation and to conserve and store energy. Both systems produce their effects by giving off certain chemical substances from the postganglionic fibers. With few exceptions, the postganglionic sympathetic fibers give off *sympathin*, which is similar to, if not identical with, adrenalin and has precisely the same effect of preparing the animal either to run away or to fight. The parasympathetic postganglionic fibers give off *acetyl-choline*, which produces a state of relaxation in the animal.

Sympathetic Nervous System. A long, ganglionated structure, the *sympathetic trunk*, lies on each side of the ventral portion of the vertebral column (Fig. 13-11). The ganglia of the sympathetic trunk are known as *chain ganglia*. They are connected by strands of nerve fibers. There is essentially one ganglion for each vertebra in the thoracic and lumbar regions. Ganglia in the cervical region are reduced so that only three are present: a *superior cervical ganglion*, a *middle cervical ganglion*, and an *inferior cervical ganglion*. Sometimes the inferior cervical ganglion tends to fuse with the first thoracic ganglion, forming the *stellate ganglion*.

The visceral ramus (ramus communicans) of a spinal nerve usually connects with a chain ganglion and typically consists of two parts, namely, a *white ramus* and a *gray ramus*. The white ramus carries both visceral sensory and preganglionic visceral motor fibers. The gray ramus carries only postganglionic visceral motor fibers.

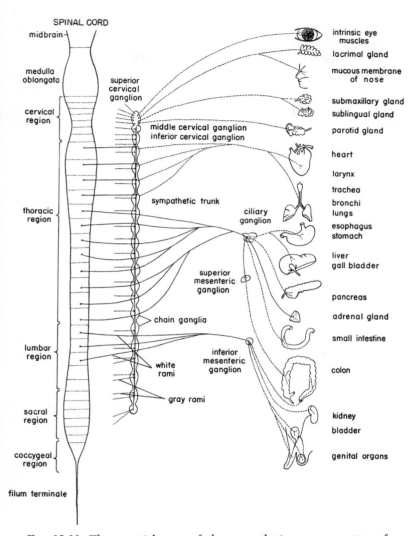

Fig. 13-11. The essential parts of the sympathetic nervous system of a mammal. Preganglionic fibers shown as solid lines, postganglionic fibers as dotted lines. (Redrawn from Weichert, *Elements of Chordate Anatomy*, McGraw-Hill, 1959, by permission.)

A sensory fiber coming from one of the visceral organs passes through the chain ganglion without synapsing and is not functionally a part of the autonomic system. A preganglionic visceral motor fiber may synapse within the ganglion or it may pass up or down the sympathetic trunk to another chain ganglion for subsequent synapsis. It might also pass through the ganglion without synapsis to one of three large *prevertebral ganglia* in the abdominal region—the *coeliac,* the *superior mesenteric,* or the *inferior mesenteric.* Either in a chain ganglion or in a prevertebral ganglion, the preganglionic fiber synapses with another neuron which gives rise to a postganglionic fiber. Each efferent visceral nerve is formed of postganglionic fibers from one of the prevertebral ganglia or from one or more of the anterior chain ganglia. Other postganglionic fibers from the chain ganglia pass through the gray rami of the rami communicans and are distributed through the dorsal or ventral rami of the spinal nerves to the blood vessels and glands of the regions innervated by these nerves.

For the most part, the preganglionic fibers of the sympathetic system tend to be short and the postganglionic fibers tend to be rather long. The sympathin produced by the sympathetic fibers is a relatively stable compound which may be distributed throughout the body by the blood stream. Hence, it generally has a widespread effect.

Parasympathetic Nervous System. The preganglionic fibers of the parasympathetic system are included in four cranial nerves (the third or oculomotor, the seventh or facial, the ninth or glossopharyngeal, and the tenth or vagus) and in the white visceral rami of the second, third, and fourth sacral nerves (Fig. 13-12). The parasympathetic differs from the sympathetic nervous system structurally in that, for the most part, the parasympathetic preganglionic fibers are very long and the relay ganglia lie within or close to the organs which the short postganglionic fibers innervate. For example, the preganglionic fibers of the oculomotor nerve terminate in the *ciliary ganglion* in the back part of the orbit, from which the postganglionic fibers pass to the intrinsic eye muscles.

The acetylcholine produced by the postganglionic fibers of the parasympathetic nervous system is a rather short-lived chemical; consequently, its effects tend to be local.

Autonomic System in Lower Vertebrates. Although, as already mentioned, the autonomic system has been best studied in mam-

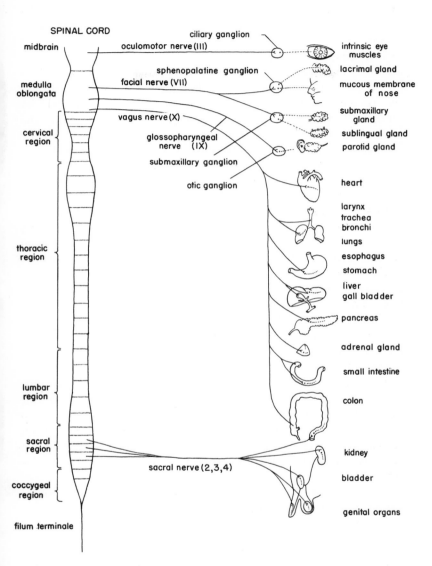

FIG. 13-12. The essential parts of the parasympathetic nervous system of a mammal. Preganglionic fibers shown as solid lines, postganglionic fibers as dotted lines. (Redrawn from Weichert, *Elements of Chordate Anatomy*, McGraw-Hill, 1959, by permission.)

mals, especially in man, our knowledge of the system in the lower vertebrates does permit some interpretation of its evolution.

Sympathetic ganglia are present in the cyclostomes, but they are not connected, so there is no true sympathetic trunk. The dorsal and ventral nerves of the lampreys remain separate and the preganglionic fibers leave the central nervous system by means of the dorsal nerve; on the other hand, in the hagfishes the two nerves have joined to form the spinal nerve proper and the sympathetic fibers presumably pass out through the ventral root. The vagus is the only nerve that contributes to the parasympathetic system of the cyclostomes; branches from it go to the heart and to part of the gut.

In the Chondrichthyes the sympathetic and parasympathetic systems are fairly well marked. The consecutive ganglia within the sympathetic system may be joined by connections, but even so the sympathetic trunk is not well defined. The parasympathetic system of the cartilaginous fishes, in addition to involving the vagus nerve, also utilizes fibers from the oculomotor, the facial, and the glossopharyngeal nerves.

The bony fishes are the first vertebrates to show a well defined sympathetic trunk with the ganglia rather consistently connected. However, only the oculomotor and vagus nerves enter into the formation of the parasympathetic system.

Among the amphibians, two situations exist. In the salamanders, the sympathetic system is essentially as it is in the amniotes, but the parasympathetic involves only cranial elements; however, in the frogs and toads the parasympathetic is composed of both cranial and sacral elements. Thus, the autonomic system of the anurans reaches a degree of complexity approaching that of the amniotes.

From what we know of the autonomic system of the reptiles and birds, it resembles closely that of the mammals.

MENINGES

The central nervous system of all the vertebrates is surrounded by membranes, the *meninges* (sing., *meninx*). All surfaces of cartilage and bone are covered with tough vascular membranes known, respectively, as the *perichondrium* and the *periosteum*.

The membrane lining the cavities of the cranium and spinal canal is known by the special name *endorachis*. It becomes involved with the meninges but is not considered a true meninx since it develops in connection with the bone or cartilage rather than with the nervous tissue of the central nervous system.

In the Agnatha, Chondrichthyes, and Osteichthyes, the protective covering of the central nervous system is simply a *primitive meninx* which forms a close union with the brain and spinal cord. Between the primitive meninx and the endorachis is a space, the *perimeningeal space,* which becomes filled with *cerebrospinal fluid.* Tiny strands of connective tissue cross the perimeningeal space to make a connection between the primitive meninx and the endorachis.

Beginning with the amphibians, the primitive meninx has divided into two layers, namely, an outer *dura mater* and an inner *pia mater,* with a space between the dura mater and the pia mater. Thus, from the central nervous system to the bone, we find a pia layer closely associated with the brain or nerve cord, then a *subdural space,* then a dura layer, then an *epidural space,* and finally the endorachis. The mammals show a further subdivision of the pia mater into an *arachnoid membrane* and a pia layer which are separated by a *subarachnoid space.* So in the mammals, we find, from the nerve cord outward: first, the pia mater; second, the subarachnoid space; third, the arachnoid membrane; fourth, the subdural space; fifth, the dura mater; sixth, the epidural space; and seventh, the endorachis. The dura mater of the brain fuses with the endorachis so that here the epidural space is eliminated.

14

Sensory Receptors

Sensory receptors essentially respond to stimuli and set up *impulses* which are transmitted by sensory neurons to the central nervous system. These impulses in the central nervous system are interpreted as *sensations*. The thalamus serves as a center for the integration of sensations, but a well developed cerebral cortex, when present, may be the seat of further sensory integration. In primitive forms of animal life, the integument in its entirety may be sensory in function, but in the vertebrates, sense organs of considerable complexity have evolved. The actual receptor cells in these organs are still usually derived from ectoderm.

Some authorities list more than thirty different senses for the human body. These, as you might imagine, have been classified in many different ways. One classification that is generally accepted divides them into *external senses* and *internal senses*. Among the external senses may be listed sight, hearing, smell, taste, temperature, etc. Internal senses include muscle position, hunger, thirst, etc. For many of the senses there are no specific receptor organs; either the nerve endings of the sensory neurons act as the receptors, or the individual receptor cells are widely scattered. This is true of the majority of internal senses and some of the external senses. However, the receptor cells of some of the internal senses (e.g., equilibrium) and a number of the external senses (e.g., sight, hearing, and smell) are gathered together with accessory structures to form discrete organs.

The sense organs that have some degree of organization in the vertebrate body are as follows: the eye, ear, olfactory organs, gustatoreceptors (taste), lateral line organs, and Jacobson's organ. (The receptors for the other senses are not organized into definite structures, and consequently they fall within the realm of physiology rather than of comparative anatomy.)

THE EYE

The vertebrate eye is a highly specialized structure which seems to have no true homologue in any of the other phyla, though a very similar eye has evolved independently in the advanced Mollusca. Since all vertebrate eyes are basically similar in structure, the human eye can well be used as an example.

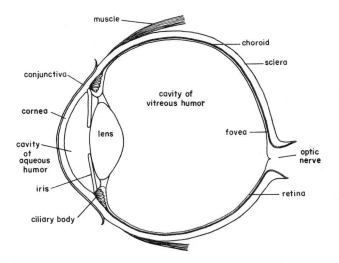

Fig. 14-1. Vertical section through the human eye. (Redrawn from Alexander, *General Zoology,* Barnes and Noble, 1951, by permission.)

Structure of Human Eye. The eye is a hollow, spherical body divided into two unequal parts by a biconcave crystalline *lens* and its supporting tissues. The smaller cavity in front of the lens is filled with a watery fluid, the *aqueous humor;* the larger cavity behind the lens is filled with a jelly-like substance, the *vitreous humor.* The covering of the eyeball is composed of three coats, or *tunics.*

External Tunic. The external tunic is a tough, fibrous layer divided into two parts. Anteriorly, there is a bulging, transparent *cornea.* The rest of the tunic consists of an opaque portion, the *sclera.* A thin epithelial membrane, the *conjunctiva,* is fused to the outer surface of the cornea. The conjunctiva is continuous with the inner lining of the eyelids. The extrinsic muscles of the eye are attached to the sclera.

Middle Tunic (Uvea). Part of the middle tunic, the heavily pigmented, vascular *choroid coat,* is closely applied to the sclera. Near the point where the cornea and sclera join, the middle tunic turns inward to form part of the *ciliary body,* a muscular and fibrous structure by which the lens is suspended, and part of the *iris*—a thin, circular disc which lies in front of the ciliary body and lens. The opening in the center of the iris is the *pupil.* The iris contains muscle fibers by which the size of the pupil, and hence the amount of light entering the eye, can be regulated.

Internal Tunic. Part of the internal tunic contributes to the formation of the ciliary body and iris. The remainder is the *retina,* which is in contact with the choroid coat and contains the actual receptor cells. These cells are of two types: *rods* and *cones.* Apparently the rods are sensitive to differences in the intensity of light, while the cones are concerned with color vision. A small area in the retina directly opposite the lens contains mostly cone cells. In man this area is marked by a yellow pigment and is known as the *macula lutea;* a shallow depression in its center, the *fovea,* marks the point of most acute vision. The point where the optic nerve joins the retina lacks receptor cells and is known as the *blind spot.*

The retinal layer is an invaginated cup formed by the expanded end of the optic nerve, which is actually an outgrowth of the brain.

Accommodation. Light rays are focused by the cornea and lens on the retina which receives the image. Many animals are able to change the focus of their eyes from objects at a distance to objects close at hand or *vice versa.* This adjustment is known as *accommodation.* Anamniotes change focus by changing the position of the lens in relation to the retina, while the amniotes change focus by altering the shape of the lens. In some anamniotes the lens is normally fixed in a forward position, which allows the animal to focus on near objects, and is drawn back to accommodate for distant objects. In other anamniotes the lens is fixed further back so that the animal normally focuses on distant objects, and the lens is drawn forward to focus on objects close at hand.

The amniote lens is normally rather flattened and the resting eye focuses on distant objects. Muscles in the ciliary body change the lens to a more rounded shape for accommodation to near objects.

Comparative Anatomy of the Eye. The vertebrate eye appears for the first time in the cyclostomes. It is already a complex structure which must have had a long evolutionary history, but we know nothing of that history.

Agnatha. Two conditions are found in the cyclostomes. The eye of the hagfish is degenerate and functionless. The eye of the lamprey, although primitive, is a fairly well developed, functional structure. It develops under the skin; at the time of metamorphosis the skin above the eye simply becomes transparent. There are no eyelids. The cornea is thin and is not fused to the skin, and the pupil is fixed in size. The eye lacks a ciliary body and the permanently spherical lens is held in place by the vitreous humor. The resting eye focuses on near objects. Change of focus is brought about by a flattening of the cornea by a special *corneal muscle;* this flattening of the cornea pushes the lens back toward the retina. Both rods and cones are present in the lamprey eye, but the rods far outnumber the cones.

Chondrichthyes. The cartilaginous fishes have eyelids which are hardly movable. Cartilage is present in the sclera. There are no intrinsic muscles in the ciliary body and the lens is permanently spherical. The resting eye focuses on distant objects. Accommodation is brought about by a small muscle, the *protractor lentis,* which swings the lens forward in the eye. The inner layer of choroid coat next to the retina contains a special layer of crystals of guanin, forming a reflecting surface, the *tapetum lucidum.* It is the reflection of light by the tapetum lucidum that makes the eye of an animal shine. The tapetum lucidum is particularly well developed in the elasmobranch fishes, but is also found in many higher vertebrates, especially nocturnal ones.

The eyes of most of the cartilaginous fishes lack cones and have only rods, though the smooth dogfish and perhaps one or two others have some cones. It is assumed that color vision is entirely lacking in the cartilaginous fishes. There is no macula lutea, but an *area centralis,* which is somewhat similar except that it lacks

pigment, is present. No fovea centralis is found in any elasmobranch eye.

Osteichthyes. There is a good deal of variation in the eyes of
the bony fishes. Here we will discuss mainly the general features
of the eye in this group. Scleral cartilages are well developed, and
in some fishes the cartilage ossifies to form one or two *scleral
bones.* Most of the bony fishes have a well developed tapetum
lucidum. In addition, the outer surface of the choroid coat is
covered with a layer of silvery guanin crystals (the *argentea*) that
makes the outer surface of the eye practically invisible in the
almost transparent baby fish, and hence serves as protective
coloration. The argentea has no known function in the adult. Both
rods and cones are developed in the eyes of bony fishes—in fact,
the teleosts have two types of cones: the regular ones and also
the "twin" cones found only in teleosts. Color vision seems to be
well developed in this group. The area centralis is well marked
in many fishes, and some of them have a true fovea. The resting
eye focuses on near objects and accommodation is brought about
by moving the spherical lens backward by means of a *retractor
lentis* muscle. A number of fishes are known as "blind" fishes; one
of them, *Ipnops,* from a depth of about 2,000 meters in the tropical
Atlantic, is the only known vertebrate with no eye structure at
all. In other blind fishes the eye is present, though it may be so
degenerate that it is microscopic and completely functionless.

Amphibia. Terrestrial adaptations include the development of
movable eyelids to protect the eye and of lubricating glands to
keep the eyeball moist. Since some amphibians are adapted to
an aquatic existence and others to a terrestrial one, we would
expect this group to show variations in the structure of the eye.
In the caecilians the eyeball lies buried beneath a transparent
area of skin to which it is sometimes fused. The permanently
aquatic salamanders lack eyelids, while in the more terrestrial
salamanders lids are present although poorly developed.

Well developed, movable lids appear for the first time in the
salientians. A frog closes its eye, not simply by moving the lids,
but by retracting the eye within the orbit by a special muscle, the
retractor bulbi. When the eyeball is pulled deeper within the
orbit, a fold of the lower lid, known as the *palpebral membrane,*
moves up to cover it entirely. When the eyeball is elevated again,
the palpebral membrane folds under the lower lid. This membrane

is probably not homologous with the true *nictitating membrane,* or third eyelid, of the other tetrapods. The salamanders with movable lids have lubricating glands in the lining of the lower lid. These glands may be antecedents of the *lacrimal gland* and the *Harderian gland (Harder's gland)* which are present in many higher vertebrates. Harder's gland appears for the first time in the inner angle of the eye of the adult frog.

The ciliary body is better developed in frogs than in the fish-like vertebrates. Fibers from it form a suspensory ligament which holds the lens in place. As in the elasmobranchs, the resting lens focuses on distant objects. To accommodate for near objects, the lens is drawn closer to the cornea by a set of protractor lentis muscles which run from the cornea to the ciliary body. There is no known mechanism for accommodation in the apode amphibians.

Strangely, no tapetum lucidum is found in frogs, though many of them have eyes that shine. The argentea is also absent. Although color vision has not been demonstrated in the amphibians, rods and cones are present in the frog's eye. Frogs have an area centralis, but none, so far as we know, has a fovea.

Reptilia. The reptiles have continued the modifications of the eye for a terrestrial existence that were initiated in the amphibians. Reptiles have well developed upper and lower lids and also a true, transparent, nictitating membrane which lies between the other eyelids and the eyeball. It is lubricated by a well developed Harder's gland. Most reptiles also have a lacrimal gland. Except in the snakes and crocodilians, the region of the sclera adjacent to the cornea contains a ring of thin, overlapping bones, the *scleral ossicles.*

The reptilian lens is somewhat flexible. For the first time, accommodation is brought about by an actual change in the shape of the lens, which is normally rather flat and adjusted for far vision. A ring of padlike processes from the enlarged ciliary body makes contact with the lens. When circular muscles in the ciliary body contract, pressure of these processes on the lens pushes it into a more rounded shape for near vision. Both rods and cones are generally present in the reptile eye, and a few of the reptiles have a well developed and conspicuous fovea. Color vision is believed to exist in some reptiles, but it is doubtful that it occurs in crocodilians or snakes.

The eye of the snake is permanently closed. The upper and lower lids are fused and the lower lid contains a transparent window (*brille*) through which the snake sees.

Aves. Birds' eyes are essentially reptilian in nature. They have movable upper and lower lids and a well developed nictitating membrane which moves independently of the other two lids. Harderian and lacrimal glands are present. Accommodation is brought about by the same mechanism as in the reptiles. Birds' eyes differ in shape from those of the other vertebrates; instead of being round or oval, they are partly concave. Only the smallest rounded portion of the eye is visible from the outside.

Scleral bones form a ring around the cornea. Behind this ring, the ciliary body is greatly expanded so that the hind part of the eyeball is larger than the forepart. Rods and cones are present and presumably color vision is widespread among birds. A unique feature is the *pecten*, a fan-shaped structure which extends into the cavity of the vitreous humor from the posterior wall near the blind spot. It is best developed in diurnal birds and most poorly developed in nocturnal forms. Its function is still a matter of speculation.

Binocular vision (in which both eyes can be focused on a single object and the fields of vision largely overlap) is well developed in some birds.

Mammalia. The eye of man (see Fig. 14-1) is a fairly typical mammalian eye. In addition to the structures already mentioned for man, eyelashes and oil-producing *Meibomian glands* are usually, but not invariably, present on the eyelids of mammals. The nictitating membrane is reduced or absent in most mammals, as is Harder's gland. Cartilage is present in the sclera of the Prototheria, but neither cartilage nor scleral ossicles are found in the other mammals. Many nocturnal forms have a well developed tapetum lucidum. Cones are lacking in some mammals, and color vision is apparently well developed only in the higher primates. The macula lutea is characteristic only of the primates, and binocular vision is best developed in them.

As in the other amniotes, accommodation in the mammalian eye is achieved by changing the shape of the lens, but the mechanism for accomplishing this differs from that of the reptiles and birds. The ciliary body is not in contact with the lens, which is suspended by fibers attached to the back edge of the ciliary region. The pull of these fibers holds the lens in a flattened condition for distant vision. Contraction of the muscles of the ciliary body brings the region of attachment of the fibers closer to the lens, the pull of the fibers on the lens is lessened, and the lens assumes a more rounded shape for focusing on near objects.

THE EAR

The vertebrate ear is a composite structure with multiple functions. The mammalian ear is commonly divided into the *inner ear,* the *middle ear,* and the *outer ear.* The inner ear, which contains the sensory receptors, is found in all vertebrates. The middle ear and outer ear are concerned with the transmission of sound waves to the inner ear and are not found in the fishlike vertebrates.

Inner Ear. The inner ear is an organ of equilibrium in all the vertebrates and an organ of hearing as well in the higher forms. Both sensations are carried to the central nervous system by fibers of the acoustic nerve.

Structure of Inner Ear. The basic structure of the vertebrate inner ear comprises two connected, membranous chambers: an upper *utriculus* and a lower *sacculus.* Except in the cyclostomes, three *semicircular ducts,* lying at right angles to each other, connect at each of their ends to the utriculus. One end of each semicircular duct bears a swelling, the *ampulla.* An *endolymphatic duct* usually leads dorsally from the sacculus to terminate in an *endolymphatic sac* within the braincase. These chambers and ducts, with various appurtenances in the different groups, form the *membranous labyrinth.* It is filled with a fluid, the *endolymph,* which has a viscosity two or three times that of water. The cartilage or bone of the skull surrounding the membranous labyrinth forms a *cartilaginous* or *bony labyrinth* which closely follows the contours of the membranous labyrinth. Between the two labyrinths lies the *perilymphatic space* filled with *perilymph* which is actually cerebrospinal fluid, for the perilymphatic space communicates with the meningeal spaces.

Movement of the endolymph within the semicircular ducts stimulates crests of sensory cells (*cristae*) in the ampullae to give an awareness of movement (*kinetic sense*). Static sense, or awareness of the position of the body at rest, results from stimulation of patches of sensory cells (*maculae*) in the utriculus and sacculus. Stimulation of the maculae is usually brought about by changes in the position of calcareous bodies, the *otoliths*, which develop within the utriculus and sacculus.

Comparative Anatomy of Inner Ear. The main evolutionary change that takes place in the inner ear is its assumption of the function of hearing in the tetrapods in addition to its primary function as an organ of equilibrium.

AGNATHA. In the cyclostomes, a small endolymphatic duct is present. The hagfish lacks a well marked distinction between the sacculus and the utriculus, and only a single, vertical semicircular duct is present. The lamprey has two vertical semicircular ducts and a slight constriction which indicates the separation of the sacculus from the utriculus.

CHONDRICHTHYES. The Chondrichthyes have three semicircular ducts as do all vertebrates above the cyclostomes. A small saclike projection from the ventral portion of the sacculus, the *lagena*, seems to be the forerunner of the auditory portion of the inner ear of the higher vertebrates. In many elasmobranchs a small tube extends upward from the membranous labyrinth to open on the dorsal surface of the head. It is sometimes inappropriately called the endolymphatic duct, but it is not homologous with this duct in other vertebrates; a more correct term is *invagination canal*. Through it fine sand grains enter the cavity of the sacculus to serve as otoliths in these non-bony vertebrates. Sea water probably passes through the invagination canal so that the membranous labyrinth of the cartilaginous fishes that have this tube is apparently filled with sea water.

OSTEICHTHYES. The invagination canal disappears and a true endolymphatic duct develops as an outgrowth from the saccular region. The lagena seems to be a little better developed in the bony fishes than it is in the cartilaginous fishes. Apparently many teleosts have some sensory receptors in the sacculus which respond to sound waves; hence a limited amount of hearing takes place in these fishes. In one group of bony fishes, the Ostariophysi, a chain of small bones, the *Weberian ossicles*, lies between the swim bladder and the perilymphatic space. These bones develop from the anterior vertebrae. The swim bladder here probably functions in some manner in equilibration and possibly also in hearing.

AMPHIBIA. The inner ear of the amphibians resembles that of the fishes in basic pattern. The division between the sacculus and utriculus is clearly marked and there are three semicircular canals. All the amphibians have endolymphatic ducts which terminate in expanded endolymphatic sacs. The lagena is somewhat better developed in the amphibians than in the fishes. In addition, some amphibians have a pouch, the *pars basilaris*, which arises from the sacculus a little behind the lagena and contains a sensory patch, the *papilla basilaris*, which seems to be concerned with hearing. While the main function of the inner ear in the amphibians is apparently still equilibration, the ability to hear has developed considerably beyond what it was in the pisciform vertebrates. Indeed, it is rather well developed in the frogs and toads.

REPTILIA, AVES, MAMMALIA. The evolution of the inner ear of the amniotes involves the further development and modification of the lagena and the papilla basilaris of the amphibian ear. The lagena and the surrounding portion of the bony labyrinth elongate to form the *cochlea proper*. The lagena, now known as the *cochlear duct*, is attached to the bony cochlea on either side, dividing its cavity into an upper portion, the *scala vestibuli*, and a lower portion, the *scala tympani*. The cavity within the cochlear duct is the *scala media*. Since the scala vestibuli and scala tympani are continuous with the cavity of the bony labyrinth, they are filled with perilympth, while the scala media is continuous with the cavity of the membranous labryinth and is filled with endolymph. Within the cochlear duct lies the *organ of Corti*, which is derived from the papilla basilaris and which bears the sensory receptor cells for hearing.

All the amniotes have a well developed cochlea. It assumes a spiral form for the first time in the crocodilians and is spiral in the birds. The cochlea reaches its greatest degree of complexity in the mammals. For example, the cochlear duct of one of the South American camels makes five complete turns.

Middle Ear. Beginning with the amphibians, this special mechanism transmits sound waves from the external environment to the membranous labyrinth of the inner ear.

Structure of Middle Ear. The middle ear essentially consists of a cavity, the *tympanic cavity*, together with one or a series of bones which cross it to transmit sound vibrations from one side to the other. The cavity of the middle ear is homologous with the

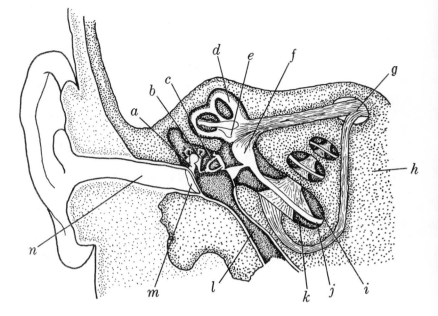

Fig. 14-2. Structure of human ear: *a*, malleus; *b*, incus; *c*, stapes; *d*, semi-circular duct; *e*, utriculus; *f*, sacculus; *g*, acoustic nerve; *h*, bone; *i*, scala vestibuli; *j*, scala media; *k*, scala tympani; *l*, Eustachian tube; *m*, tympanic membrane; *n*, external auditory meatus.

spiracle of the elasmobranch fishes. In the formation of the tetrapod middle ear, the first pharyngeal pouch pushes outward and the superficial ectoderm pushes inward until the endoderm comes into contact with the ectoderm. The pouch fails to rupture so that a membrane composed of ectoderm and endoderm separates the pouch from the outside. Later, some mesodermal tissue pushes in between these two layers to form a true *tympanic membrane,* or *eardrum.* The portion of the pharyngeal pouch immediately adjacent to the eardrum is expanded to form the *tympanic chamber,* while the portion nearest the pharynx is constricted to form the *Eustachian tube* which leads into the pharynx by a small opening. The Eustachian tube serves to balance atmospheric pressure on the two sides of the tympanic membrane.

The scala vestibuli of the cochlea connects with the cavity of the middle ear by means of a small oval window, the *fenestra ovalis.* Between the tympanic membrane and the fenestra ovalis lie the middle ear bones, or *ossicles.* Sound waves set up vibrations in the tympanic membrane which are transmitted to these bones and thence to the fluid of the cochlea through the fenestra ovalis. Another small opening, the *fenestra rotunda,* which is covered by a delicate membrane, lies between the scala tympani and the tympanic cavity.

Comparative Anatomy of Middle Ear. The major evolutionary change that takes place in the middle ear is the increase in the number of bones by which sound is transmitted from the tympanic membrane to the fenestra ovalis.

AMPHIBIA. Two situations exist in the amphibians. The salamanders, apodans, and a few frogs lack tympanic membrane, tympanic cavity, and Eustachian tube, but do have the fenestra ovalis plugged by a bone, the *columella.* This bone is derived from the hyomandibular of the pisciform vertebrates and lies within a ligament which runs from the fenestra ovalis to the squamosal and quadrate bones. In addition to the columella, most amphibians have another cartilaginous or bony element, the *operculum,* which fits into the fenestra ovalis along with the columella. It does not seem to be present in any other vertebrate. In a few amphibians, such as *Necturus,* the columella and the operculum fuse. In the salamanders, sound vibrations are apparently transmitted to the columella and operculum by means of veins and sinuses in the head. The auditory sense seems to be rather poorly developed in the apodans and salamanders.

Most frogs and toads have a well developed middle ear cavity, together with a tympanic membrane and Eustachian tube. Usually the tympanic membrane lies flush with the surface of the head. (In one of the frogs, it is at the base of a pit corresponding to the external auditory meatus of the birds and mammals.) In the anurans, vibrations are transmitted from the tympanic membrane to the fenestra ovalis by means of the columella.

REPTILIA. The middle ear structure of many reptiles is similar to that of the frogs. The columella is usually divided into two parts: the *stapes proper* abuts on the fenestra ovalis, and the *extracolumella* abuts on the tympanic membrane. Snakes and some lizards lack the middle ear cavity, Eustachian tube, and tympanic membrane; sound vibrations pass from the jaws through the columella to the fenestra ovalis.

In the crocodilians (and in the tongueless toads among the amphibians), the Eustachian tubes come together to open into the pharynx by a single median aperture. The tympanic membrane usually lies flush with the surface of the head, but in some of the lizards it lies at the base of a shallow ear pit.

AVES. Birds have a well developed middle ear with the columella divided into stapes proper and extracolumella. The Eustachian tubes open by a single median aperture into the pharynx. The tympanic membrane is not at the surface but is located some distance from the surface at the end of a narrow passage, the *external auditory meatus.*

MAMMALIA. Mammals have three bones forming a chain across the tympanic cavity; these are (from tympanic membrane to fenestra ovalis) the *malleus,* the *incus,* and the *stapes.* The stapes is homologous with the columella, which in turn was derived from the hyomandibular of the lower vertebrates; the malleus is homologous with the articular bone, and the incus homologous with the quadrate bone. In all the mammals the Eustachian tubes open separately into the pharynx and in all the tympanic membrane is situated at the end of a fairly deep external auditory meatus. (See Fig. 14-2, p. 190.)

Outer Ear. The outer ear is the entire portion of the ear external to the tympanic membrane. It consists of the external auditory meatus and, in the mammals, of a fleshy external ear known as the *pinna,* or *auricle.* As noted above, one of the frogs and a number of lizards have the tympanic membrane located at the base of a pit which is the forerunner of the external auditory meatus. In general, though, a well developed meatus is found only in the birds and mammals. Some birds have tufts of feathers which function as a pinna in directing sound waves into the auditory canal. The mammalian pinna varies widely in shape; it tends to be reduced or absent in burrowing forms and in the aquatic mammals.

CHEMORECEPTORS

Vertebrates have a number of sensory receptors that are stimulated by chemical substances in solution. The fishlike vertebrates and the amphibians with their moist skins have chemoreceptors scattered over the entire surface of the body. Other chemoreceptors are localized in the nasal structures, the mouth, and Jacobson's organ—these are the only chemoreceptors present in the dry-skinned amniotes.

Olfactoreceptors. The olfactoreceptors comprise sensory neurons imbedded in an olfactory epithelium which lines a nasal chamber situated in the anterior part of the head. The axons of these neurons form the olfactory nerve. Mucous glands are present in the epithelium of the tetrapods, both to protect it and to provide moisture. This moisture is necessary since in both of the chemical senses, smell and taste, substances must be in solution before they can stimulate the sensory neurons.

The nasal passages of the tetrapods are correlated with respiration as well as with olfaction (see discussion under the respiratory system, p. 106).

Agnatha. The cyclostomes have a single, median naris leading into a blind *nasal sac*. (This condition is a modified one since the nasal passages are double in the larvae and the nasal sac has paired olfactory nerves associated with it.) From the anterior end of this blind sac a unique pouch, the *nasopharyngeal pouch*, leads posteriorly. In the lamprey it ends blindly in the region of the second gill slit, but in the hagfish it makes a connection with the pharynx. So far as is known, it has no counterpart in any other class of vertebrates. It is believed to be a structure that has split off from the stomodaeum.

Chondrichthyes. The cartilaginous fishes have paired nasal sacs, as do all vertebrates except the cyclostomes. The nostrils are on the ventral side of the proboscis. Each nostril is partially divided by a flap of skin so that water tends to come in one side of the the nostril and pass out the other. The olfactory epithelium is thrown into numerous well developed folds (*Schneiderian folds*) which greatly increase the olfactory surface. In these fishes the sense of smell is probably the best developed of all the senses.

Osteichthyes. The nostrils of the bony fishes are usually on the anterolateral surface of the head. The nasal sac may vary from a small, blind pit lined with olfactory epithelium to a well developed, U-shaped, tubular structure in which the nostril, instead of being simply partially divided by a flap of skin, is split into two separate openings, an incurrent and an excurrent one. Like the sharks and their allies, many bony fishes have well developed

Schneiderian folds. As was mentioned under the respiratory system, it is the choanate fishes that first develop a true choana, or internal naris, so that a passageway from the external naris on the surface of the face to the pharynx is formed.

Amphibia. In all the amphibians, the olfactory membrane is located within the passageway from the external naris to the pharynx. Larval and permanently aquatic forms have valves at the choanal openings to regulate the direction of the flow of water. Metamorphosed, terrestrial adults tend to lose these valves and to develop new ones at the external ends of the nasal passages. These terrestrial forms have glandular masses whose secretions keep the olfactory epithelium moist. In some amphibians, a shelflike fold of the lateral wall into the nasal passageway foreshadows the development of the *bony conchae,* or *turbinal folds,* of the higher vertebrates.

Reptilia. The nasal passages of the reptiles show an increasing tendency to become divided into an anterior respiratory portion and a posterior olfactory portion. In most reptiles, a single, swollen ingrowth, or concha, develops from the ethmoid bone in the lateral wall of each nasal passage. It increases the surface over which the olfactory epithelium may form. Crocodilians have three conchae.

Aves. The sense of smell is not well developed in the birds, but they retain the three conchae of the crocodilians. They have in each nasal passage an anterior *vestibular concha* and smaller *middle* and *superior conchae.* The vestibular concha never bears any olfactory epithelium, and although olfactory epithelium does cover the middle concha for a time after hatching, it soon disappears. The only olfactory epithelium in the adult is that investing the superior concha.

Mammalia. The nasal passage of the mammal is divided into three more or less distinct portions. The anterior vestibular region is lined with skin which becomes continuous on the inside with the mucous membrane. Sebaceous glands and hairs are present in this region. The respiratory region comprises the greater portion of the nasal passages. It is here that the air is warmed and moistened. The Schneiderian membrane is located in the innermost, or olfactory, region.

Most mammals have the conchae elaborated into a complicated series of folds, the *turbinate bones.* They are derived from the ethmoid, maxillary, and nasal bones and are consequently known as the *ethmoturbinate, maxilloturbinate,* and *nasoturbinate bones.* The epithelial covering of the maxilloturbinates and nasoturbinates is not olfactory but simply functions to warm and moisten the air on its way through the nasal passage. The Schneiderian membrane is supported by the ethmoturbinates. The sense of smell varies with the development of the Schneiderian membrane. In man it is a poorly developed structure, but in many of the mammals it is quite highly folded and complex; in these forms the olfactory sense reaches its maximum development.

Jacobson's Organ. Jacobson's organ, or the *vomeronasal organ* as it is sometimes called, is an accessory olfactory organ which appears first in the amphibians. In them it is a blind sac connected by a thin duct to the nasal chamber. It is lacking in the aquatic salamanders, *Necturus* and *Proteus.* Jacobson's organ is best developed in the reptiles, particularly in *Sphenodon,* and the snakes and lizards. In the Squamata, the duct, instead of being connected with the nasal chamber, opens into the roof of the mouth. Other reptiles and birds lack Jacobson's organ as adults, though it appears during embryonic development. There is variation in the mammals. Monotremes have a fairly well developed Jacobson's organ and it is present as a small but distinct structure in a number of the Theria, especially the more primitive forms such as the marsupials, the insectivores, and the rodents. In other mammals, such as man, it is present only during embryonic development.

Jacobson's organ is supplied by branches from three cranial nerves: O (terminal); I (olfactory); and V (trigeminal).

Gustatoreceptors. Taste is a chemical sense closely related to smell. The sensory receptor cells for taste, together with supporting cells, are gathered together in bundles known as *taste buds* because of their superficial resemblance to unfolded leaf buds. Gustatoreceptors transmit impulses through cranial nerves VII (facial), IX (glossopharyngeal), and X (vagus). The sense of taste is rather restricted in man; generally only four distinct tastes (bitter, sweet, salty, and sour) are recognized, though some authorities would add a fifth (metallic).

Comparative Anatomy of Gustatoreceptors. Taste buds of all vertebrates are very similar in structure, varying chiefly in number and distribution.

AGNATHA. The cyclostomes have taste buds on the surface of the head and in the lining of the pharynx.

CHONDRICHTHYES. In the cartilaginous fishes, the only epithelium bearing taste buds is that lining the mouth and pharynx.

OSTEICHTHYES. There is a good deal of variation in the distribution of taste buds among the fishes. Some forms, such as suckers and catfishes, have the taste buds distributed over the entire body surface including the fins and tail. Others may have them on the surface of the head as well as in the lining of the mouth and pharynx. In the lungfishes, taste buds are not present on the outer surface of the body, but are restricted to the lining of the mouth and pharynx and to the tongue.

AMPHIBIA. The amphibians, like all the terrestrial vertebrates, lack taste buds on the outer surface of the body. Taste buds are restricted to the epithelium lining the roof of the mouth, the jaws, and the surface of the tongue. Some salamanders have been reported to be able to distinguish different tastes.

REPTILIA. The reptiles have taste buds on the lining of the pharyngeal region, but few, if any, are present on the surface of the tongue.

AVES. Most birds have the taste buds restricted to the lining of the mouth and pharynx, with none present on the corneous tongue. However, the fleshy tongue of the parrot bears numerous taste buds.

MAMMALIA. In mammals, taste buds may be present in the linings of the mouth and pharynx and on the tongue. They seem to be lacking in the whales.

LATERAL LINE ORGANS

The lateral line system occurs only in the pisciform vertebrates and larval and aquatic amphibians. Apparently its function is to make the animal aware of currents and vibrations in the water.

The functional units of the lateral line system are the *neuromasts,* small groups of sensory cells surrounded by supporting cells, which are usually arranged in rows. The neuromasts are on the surface of the body in the cyclostomes and aquatic amphibians. Most fishes have the neuromasts in grooves which are usually closed over to form tubes. The tubes open to the surface by small pores. There is some variation in the arrangement of the rows or tubes containing the neuromasts, but in general they tend to be grouped around the head with (in the adult) a single lateral row, the *lateral line*, running along each side of the body. The lateral line organs are innervated by branches from the seventh, ninth, and tenth cranial nerves. The seventh (facial) and ninth (glossopharyngeal) nerves are associated with the rows or tubes around the head region, while the tenth (vagus) nerve is associated with the lateral line proper.

15

Endocrine System

Endocrine glands occur in all vertebrates. Together they make up a rather definite organ system which is concerned primarily with the regulation and co-ordination of bodily activities. They function through the production of chemical substances known as *hormones*. The endocrine glands have one characteristic in common; their secretions are released directly to the tissue fluid and are transported by the blood rather than being carried through special ducts. Endocrine glands are hence sometimes known as *ductless glands*.

We will here concern ourselves only with the rather well-known endocrine glands that occur widely throughout the vertebrates. Consequently, some structures with an endocrine function will be omitted. For example, the mammalian placenta functions in part as an endocrine gland, but since it is characteristic only of the eutherian mammals, it will not be discussed here. Endocrine glands we will consider are the thyroid, the parathyroids, the adrenals, the pancreas, the pituitary, and, briefly, the gonads.

THYROID GLAND

The thyroid gland seems to be nearly as typical of the vertebrates as are the hollow, dorsal nerve cord and the pharyngeal slits. It consists of a number of small sacs, or *follicles*, of different sizes all bound together by thin strands of connective tissue. It originates as a single, median, ventral outgrowth of the pharynx, though it is frequently secondarily divided into two lobes which may be completely separated. *Thyroxin*, the hormone produced by the thyroid, controls the rate of metabolism of the body. Iodine is a major component of this hormone. If sufficient environmental iodine is not available, the thyroid gland may enlarge, a condition known as *endemic goiter*.

Agnatha. In the ammocoetes larva of the lamprey, a *subpharyngeal gland* (sometimes called the *endostyle*) lies beneath the floor of the pharynx, between the gill pouches. At the time of metamorphosis, some of the cells of this gland change their form and become arranged like cells of typical thyroid follicles. Other cells in the subpharyngeal gland do not make this change; therefore, probably only part of the gland is really homologous with the thyroid of the other vertebrates. The thyroid of the hagfish is composed of glandular tissue imbedded in fat beneath the pharynx and between the gill pouches.

Chondrichthyes and Osteichthyes. In all the fishes, both cartilaginous and bony, the thyroid gland appears early in embryonic development. The thyroid of the adult elasmobranch is a single organ located posterior to the mandibular symphysis. The lobes are usually separated in the bony fishes so that the gland appears to be a paired structure. The lobes lie on each side near the first branchial arch. Fishes raised in hatcheries in which there is not adequate iodine in the water or in the diet have been known to become goitrous.

Amphibia. The thyroid glands of the amphibians are also paired. They lie at the bases of the angles of the jaw in salamanders and on each side of the hyoid apparatus in frogs. There seems to be a correlation between the number of follicles and the size of the animal in any individual species. A large animal has a greater number of follicles than a smaller animal of the same species. Physiologically the thyroid gland has been studied extensively in the amphibians. It has a very pronounced effect on the metamorphosis of the tadpoles and larvae and on the shedding of the stratum corneum.

Reptilia. The thyroid of the snakes, turtles, and crocodilians is a median, unpaired structure lying in front of the pericardial cavity. It is paired in the lizards and lies in a more anterior position, ventral to the trachea. As in the amphibians, the thyroid of the reptiles has been shown to have a pronounced effect upon shedding of the outer layer of skin (ecdysis).

Aves. The thyroid of the birds presents no unusual features. It is paired, the lobes lying on either side of the trachea near the region where it divides into the bronchi.

Mammalia. The mammalian thyroid is a paired structure lying on each side of the base of the trachea with the lobes connected across the ventral side of the trachea by a narrow *isthmus*. Deficiency of thyroid production in man brings about such conditions as cretinism, myxedema, and endemic goiter, while overproduction of the hormone results in the condition known as *exophthalmic goiter*.

PARATHYROID GLANDS

Early in the development of all the vertebrates, small masses of epithelial cells appear near the ends of some of the visceral pouches, usually the third and fourth. In the tetrapods, these cell masses develop into the parathyroid glands, so called because in mammals they usually lie alongside the thyroid gland.

Agnatha. The cyclostomes have small, epithelial, endodermal structures near the ends of all the visceral pouches. They develop no further than small buds and their significance is unknown.

Chondrichthyes and Osteichthyes. Like the cyclostomes, both the cartilaginous and the bony fishes have glandular, endodermal, epithelial masses developed in association with the visceral pouches. Their function remains obscure.

Amphibia. In the amphibians, the first structures that can be positively identified as parathyroid glands appear. They are derived from the ventral portions of the third and fourth pairs of pharyngeal pouches. Salamanders usually have two or three on each side lying lateral to the aortic arches; occasionally, however, only a single pair is present. The parathyroids of the frogs and toads are small, rounded bodies, two on each side, near the posterior end of the hyoid cartilage. Presumably, these glands function in the amphibians, as they do in the mammals, to control the level of calcium and phosphorus in the blood.

Reptilia. The parathyroids of the reptiles are also derived from near the ventral ends of visceral pouches three and four. Two pairs are present. In most reptiles they lie somewhat posterior and lateral to the thyroids, but in the snakes they lie nearer to the base of the skull.

Aves. Birds have one or two pairs of parathyroids derived from ventral outgrowths from visceral pouches three and four. They lie slightly posterior to, or occasionally on the dorsal surface of, the thyroid gland.

Mammalia. The parathyroids are best known in the mammals. They develop from the dorsal margins of visceral pouches three and four, rather than from the ventral margins as in the other tetrapods. There are usually two on each side, though occasionally more than two pairs may be found. They lie adjacent to the thyroid gland, or are sometimes imbedded in the thyroid tissue. The parathyroids of mammals have been well studied functionally and have been shown to control the level of calcium and phosphorus salts in the blood.

ADRENAL GLANDS

The adrenal glands are so named because in man they happen to lie close to the anterior ends of the kidneys. However, their embryonic development and distribution in the lower vertebrates show that their two parts, the *medulla* and the *cortex*, are not originally closely related anatomically. The medulla of the mammalian adrenal has been shown to be derived from ectodermal neural crest cells; it is the homologue of the *chromaffin bodies* of the lower vertebrates. On the other hand, the cortex of the mammalian adrenal is derived from mesoderm and is the homologue of the *interrenal bodies* of the lower vertebrates.

Agnatha. Two conditions are found in the cyclostomes. In the hagfish, chromaffin bodies are present as tiny, isolated strips of tissue along the course of the dorsal aorta from the anterior end of the gill region to the base of the tail. No interrenal tissue has been described for the hagfish. The lamprey, *Petromyzon,* has both interrenal and chromaffin tissue. The interrenal tissue is arranged in a series of small bodies situated along the blood vessels associated with the opisthonephric kidneys. The chromaffin bodies are arranged as in the hagfish. Extract from this tissue produces the same stimulant effect in a cat as does the adrenalin produced by the medulla of the mammalian adrenal gland.

Chondrichthyes. The interrenal bodies of the cartilaginous fishes lie between the posterior ends of the kidneys. The sharks and their allies have the interrenal tissue consolidated into a single, unpaired structure, while in the rays the interrenal bodies are paired. The chromaffin bodies are paired and located along the parietal branches of the dorsal aorta.

Osteichthyes. The interrenal and chromaffin bodies are still separate in the bony fishes. The interrenal bodies of the teleosts are paired and lie along the surface of the kidneys; sometimes they are partially imbedded in the kidney tissue. The chromaffin bodies lie in the walls of the postcardinal veins. No interrenal bodies have been described for the dipnoans, in which the chromaffin bodies are arranged around the parietal branches of the aorta as well as in the walls of the postcardinal vein.

Amphibia. The close anatomical relationship between the interrenal and chromaffin elements which is characteristic of the tetrapods appears for the first time in the amphibians. In the salamanders, the components are intermingled and located in strips of tissue along the length of the opisthonephric kidney. In the frogs and toads, the elements form a band of yellowish tissue on the ventral surface of the kidney. The interrenal elements are arranged in columns of cells with the chromaffin cells irregularly distributed throughout the gland.

Reptilia. The large adrenals of the reptiles lie anterior to the kidneys, around the vena cava. Most reptiles have the interrenal and chromaffin elements closely intermingled, but in a few of them the chromaffin elements are concentrated on the dorsal side of the gland while the interrenal elements are concentrated on the ventral side.

Aves. The adrenal glands of the birds are yellowish bodies lying on either side of the vena cava immediately anterior to the kidneys. The interrenal and chromaffin elements are closely associated; slivers of chromaffin tissue lie between masses of interrenal tissue.

Mammalia. The mammalian adrenals are situated anterior to the kidneys, sometimes in close apposition to them. The gland comprises a central portion, the medulla, containing the chromaffin elements, and an outer cortex containing the interrenal elements. The egg-laying mammals do not show as sharp a distinction between the cortex and the medulla as do the marsupials and placentals. In a few species of mammals, a layer of connective tissue separates the cortex from the medulla. The medulla produces the hormone *adrenalin,* or *epinephrine,* which is structurally similar to the sympathin produced by the sympathetic nervous system. (Remember that the medulla arises embryonically from neural crest cells.) Adrenalin also resembles sympathin in effect; it raises the blood pressure, strengthens the heart beat, and in general prepares the animal to meet conditions of stress. The cortex produces a large number of hormones, the *adrenocorticoids*. Among other effects, they control the salt and water balance of the body and influence carbohydrate metabolism. An animal can survive the removal of the medullary portions of the adrenals, but the removal of all cortical tissue is fatal.

PANCREAS

The vertebrate pancreas has a dual role. It is both an exocrine gland, supplying enzymes to the digestive system by means of the pancreatic ducts, and an endocrine gland, supplying hormones to the body. Two hormones, *insulin* and *glucagon,* which have been identified from pancreatic secretions, control the sugar balance of the blood. The cells producing these hormones are gathered together in clumps known as *islands of Langerhans.*

Agnatha. No discrete pancreas is apparent in the cyclostomes, although cells buried in the liver and in the wall of the intestine seem to be homologous to the endocrine tissue of the pancreas of the higher vertebrates.

Chondrichthyes. The cartilaginous fishes have a fairly well defined pancreas. In the spiny dogfish, for example, it consists of a long, narrow, dorsal lobe and a round, flattened, ventral lobe connected by means of a short isthmus. In the cartilaginous fishes, the endocrine cells of the islands of Langerhans are reported to border a cavity or hollow within the pancreas.

Osteichthyes. The pancreas of the bony fishes is usually rather diffuse. The islands of Langerhans are fewer in number and proportionately much larger than in the mammals; indeed, they can be seen by the naked eye. Many of the bony fishes have a separate, quite enlarged, incapsulated island of Langerhans lying near the region of the gall bladder. It seems to have little relation to the rest of the pancreatic tissue. In some species pancreatic endocrine tissue can be identified only in this *principal island.*

Tetrapod Classes. In the amphibians, reptiles, birds, and mammals, the pancreas varies somewhat in form from species to species, but shows little correlation according to class. The islands of Langerhans are scattered among the remaining tissues of the pancreas and no striking or unusual features may be noted.

PITUITARY BODY

The pituitary body, or *hypophysis cerebri,* of the mammals is made up of four parts derived from two embryonic sources. From the floor of the diencephalon, an outgrowth, the *infundibulum,* extends ventrally. This gives rise to the *posterior lobe,* or *neurohypophysis,* of the pituitary body. At the time the infundibulum is developing, an outpouching from the dorsal roof of the stomodaeum, *Rathke's pouch,* grows upward and becomes separated from the stomodaeum. It gives rise to the *anterior* and *intermediate lobes* of the pituitary (*adenohypophysis*). The original cavity of Rathke's pouch usually persists as a small cavity, the *hypophyseal cleft.*

In addition to the three lobes of the pituitary, a mass of vascular tissue, also derived from Rathke's pouch, may form a collar-like structure around the base of the infundibulum. This structure, the *pars tuberalis,* occurs in most vertebrates but is absent from some, such as the snakes and lizards. Its functional significance, if any, is unknown.

Various hormones are produced by the pituitary. Many of them function in stimulating hormone production by other endocrine organs. Thus, the *thyrotropic hormone* of the pituitary stimulates the production of thyroxin by the thyroid. On the other hand, the presence of an excess of thyroxin in the blood inhibits the production of more thyrotropic hormone by the pituitary. The posterior lobe apparently does not itself secrete hormones. Secretions associated with it (such as *vasopressin* which raises the blood pressure) are formed in neurosecretory cells in the hypothalamus and pass down axon tracts of the infundibulum to the posterior lobe for storage and transfer to the blood.

Agnatha. The nasopharyngeal pouch already described in relation to the olfactoreceptors of the cyclostomes (see p. 193) develops from an embryonic *nasohypophyseal stalk* which extends beneath the forebrain. Small masses of cells differentiate from the stalk to form the anterior and intermediate lobes of the pituitary. The nasopharyngeal pouch thus seems to be a stomodaeal pouch homologous with Rathke's pouch, but opening directly to the outside instead of into the mouth. In the cyclostomes, the infundibulum is not distinct. The posterior lobe of the pituitary is represented by a plate of tissue on the floor of the diencephalon. In the hagfish, this plate is separated from the adenohypophysis by a layer of connective tissue.

Chondrichthyes and Osteichthyes. The pituitary of the fishes is a conspicuous structure. The infundibulum is distinct. It usually develops a pair of enlarged, lateral, inferior lobes and a dorsal, thin-walled *saccus vasculosus* as well as the neurohypophysis. The adenohypophysis is not clearly divided into anterior and intermediate lobes. In *Polypterus* the adenohypophysis is still connected with the mouth cavity by means of a persistent duct. Rathke's pouch in the teleosts is from the start a solid structure which never has a cavity.

Amphibia. The pituitary body of the amphibians resembles that of the teleosts in that Rathke's pouch is solid. In addition, the anterior lobe of the amphibians is extremely prominent but has come to lie posterior to the other parts of the pituitary.

Reptilia. The main peculiarity shown by the pituitary of the reptiles is the fact that the infundibular stalk is quite long so that the pituitary body itself extends posterior to the diencephalon. As mentioned above, the pars tuberalis is conspicuously absent in the snakes and lizards.

Aves. Perhaps the most striking feature of the pituitary body of the birds is that the adenohypophysis never gives rise to an intermediate lobe; hence, in this group the pituitary is formed only of anterior and posterior lobes. Furthermore, the structure is solid in the adult bird, although a small hypophyseal cleft is present embryonically.

Mammalia. The pituitary of the mammals is fairly typical of that of the other vertebrates. The anterior and intermediate lobes are separated by the hypophyseal cleft. Some mammals lack a discrete intermediate lobe but the anterior and posterior lobes are separated by connective tissue.

GONADS

The vertebrate gonads are dual organs that are both cytogenic, or cell producing, and endocrinic, or hormone producing. The hormones formed, whether by the male testis or by the female ovary, have to do with secondary sexual characteristics, sexual cycles, and the development of accessory sex organs.

In mammals, the hormones of the ovary, *estrogens,* are produced by the cells of the Graafian follicles. The male hormone, *testosterone,* is produced by interstitial cells lying between the seminiferous tubules. Little is known of the source of the sex hormones in other vertebrates. (For discussions of the comparative anatomy of the gonads, see Chap. 11, p. 121.)

Summary of Vertebrate Characters and Advances

The following summary lists some of the important character-istics of, and the structural advances shown by the various groups of living vertebrates discussed in this Outline. Characters unique to a group are given in **boldface** type while characters that repre-sent the first appearance of a structural advance are *italicized*. In general, structural advances listed for one group may be as-sumed to be present in following groups.

PHYLUM CHORDATA

a. **Notochord**
b. **Hollow, dorsal nerve cord**
c. **Pharyngeal slits or pouches**

Subphylum Vertebrata

a. *Anterior end of nerve cord expanded to form brain*
b. *Cranium*
c. *Vertebrae*

CLASS AGNATHA

ORDER CYCLOSTOMATA
a. **No jaws**
b. **No paired appendages** (paired appendages have been secondarily lost in some other groups)
c. **A single median nostril**
d. Cartilaginous skeleton
e. No scales

f. Two-chambered heart
g. Adult kidney pronephros or opisthonephros
h. Ten pairs of cranial nerves
i. **One or two semicircular ducts in inner ear**

CLASS CHONDRICHTHYES

a. *True jaws*
b. *Paired appendages*
c. *Paired nares*
d. Cartilaginous skeleton
e. **Placoid dermal scales**
f. Spiral valve in intestine
g. Two-chambered heart
h. Adult kidney opisthonephros
i. **Claspers formed from pelvic fins of male**
j. Ten pairs of cranial nerves
k. *Three semicircular ducts in inner ear*

ORDER ELASMOBRANCHII
    a. Spiracle
    b. Gill slits open separately to outside
    c. Hyostylic jaw
    d. Cloaca

ORDER HOLOCEPHALI
    a. No spiracle
    b. Fleshy operculum covering gill slits
    c. Autostylic jaw
    d. No cloaca

CLASS OSTEICHTHYES

a. *Bony skeleton*
b. **Bony operculum**
c. **Dermal scales ganoid, cycloid, or ctenoid**
d. *Dermatocranium*
e. Heart usually two-chambered
f. Adult kidney usually opisthonephros, occasionally pronephros
g. Ten pairs of cranial nerves

Subclass Actinopterygii

   a. Nostrils usually not connected with mouth
   b. Paired fins supported by horny rays, usually without fleshy lobe at base
   c. Two-chambered heart

Superorder Chondrostei

   a. Endoskeleton largely cartilaginous
   b. Spiracle
   c. Teeth lacking
   d. Hyostylic jaw
   e. Clavicle
   f. Spiral valve in intestine
   g. Scales ganoid, if present

Superorder Holostei

   a. Occipital region of cranium bony
   b. No spiracle
   c. Teeth present
   d. Hyostylic or modified hyostylic jaw
   e. Clavicle lacking
   f. Spiral valve in intestine vestigial
   g. Scales ganoid to cycloid

Superorder Teleostei

   a. Skull largely bony
   b. No spiracle
   c. Teeth present
   d. Hyostylic or modified hyostylic jaw
   e. Clavicle lacking
   f. No spiral valve in intestine
   g. Scales cycloid to ctenoid

Subclass Choanichthyes

   a. *Nostrils usually connected with mouth*
   b. Paired fins with fleshy lobe at base, supported by bony elements
   c. *Air bladder lunglike and may be used in respiration*
   d. *Three-chambered heart*

Order Dipnoi

   a. No spiracle
   b. Premaxillary and maxillary bones absent

ORDER CROSSOPTERYGII
- a. Spiracle present
- b. Premaxillary and maxillary bones present

CLASS AMPHIBIA

- a. Respiration in adult usually by lungs
- b. Metamorphosis usually occurs
- c. Integument usually without scales
- d. Two occipital condyles
- e. *Pentadactyl limbs*
- f. Adult kidney opisthonephros
- g. Ten pairs of cranial nerves

Superorder Lepospondyli
- a. Centrum of vertebra spool-shaped; not preformed in cartilage
- b. Tail present

ORDER TRACHYSTOMATA
- a. Hind limbs lacking
- b. No metamorphosis
- c. No scales

ORDER CAUDATA
- a. Both front and hind limbs present
- b. Metamorphosis usual
- c. No scales

ORDER APODA
- a. No limbs
- b. Metamorphosis
- c. Minute dermal scales in primitive forms

Superorder Salientia

ORDER ANURA
- a. Centrum of vertebra preformed in cartilage
- b. Tail absent

CLASS REPTILIA

- a. *Epidermal scales*

b. One occipital condyle
c. Heart usually three-chambered
d. *Adult kidney metanephros*
e. *Amniote egg*
f. *Twelve pairs of cranial nerves*

Subclass Anapsida

ORDER TESTUDINATA
a. No teeth
b. Jaw invested with horny covering
c. No dorsal or lateral openings in skull
d. **Shell comprised of plastron and carapace**
e. Copulatory organ single

Subclass Lepidosauria

a. Body covered with deciduous, epidermal scales
b. Teeth present
c. Both dorsal and lateral openings in skull

ORDER RHYNCHOCEPHALIA
a. No copulatory organ
b. **Well developed parietal eye**
c. Gastralia
d. Cloacal opening (vent) a transverse slit

ORDER SQUAMATA
a. **Paired copulatory organs**
b. Parietal eye, if present, not well developed
c. No gastralia
d. Cloacal opening a transverse slit

SUBORDER LACERTILIA
a. Visible external ear openings
b. Eyelids usually movable
c. **Tail generally rather fragile and detachable**
d. Limbs usually present

SUBORDER SERPENTES
a. No external ear openings
b. Eyelids immovable and transparent
c. Tail not readily detachable
d. Limbs absent

Subclass Archosauria

ORDER CROCODILIA
- a. Copulatory organ single
- b. Cloacal opening a longitudinal slit
- c. *Four-chambered heart*
- d. Gastralia
- e. *Teeth set in sockets*
- f. Both dorsal and lateral skull openings
- g. *Secondary bony palate*
- h. *True cerebral cortex*

CLASS AVES

- a. **Feathers**
- b. **Light, hollow bones**
- c. Wings
- d. One occipital condyle
- e. **Right systemic arch persists, left one disappears**
- f. *Endothermic*

CLASS MAMMALIA

- a. **Hair**
- b. **Mammary glands**
- c. Claws, nails, or hoofs
- d. Single penis
- e. Two occipital condyles
- f. **Left systemic arch persists, right one disappears**

Subclass Prototheria
- a. Oviparous
- b. No nipples or teats
- c. Cloaca
- d. Urethra not in penis

Subclass Theria
- a. Viviparous
- b. *Nipples or teats present*
- c. No cloaca (except in pika)
- d. Urethra passes through penis

Infraclass Metatheria
 a. **Marsupium present**
 b. Usually no placental attachment
 c. **Paired vaginae**

Infraclass Eutheria
 a. No marsupium
 b. Allantoic placenta
 c. Single vagina

ORDER INSECTIVORA
 a. Small size
 b. Prism-shaped molar teeth
 c. Elongated snout

ORDER CHIROPTERA
 a. Anterior limb modified for flight
 b. Keeled sternum

ORDER PRIMATES
 a. Well developed cerebrum
 b. **Eyes completely encircled by bony orbits**
 c. Eyes directed forward
 d. Thumbs usually opposable

ORDER CARNIVORA
 a. Three pairs of incisor teeth
 b. Canine teeth well developed
 c. Clavicle poorly developed or absent

ORDER PERISSODACTYLA
 a. Hoofed forms with an odd number of toes
 b. Axis of leg passes through middle toe
 c. Gall bladder absent

ORDER ARTIODACTYLA
 a. Hoofed forms with an even number of toes
 b. Axis of leg passes between third and fourth toes
 c. True horns or antlers may be present
 d. Incisors and canines usually absent from upper jaw (except in pigs)

ORDER CETACEA
 a. Anterior appendages flippers

b. No claws
c. Nasal openings on top of head
d. Pelvic appendages lacking

ORDER RODENTIA

a. Incisor teeth chisel-shaped, grow throughout life
b. Canine teeth lacking
c. Claws

Appendix II

Glossary

We have largely restricted this glossary to terms that have general significance, avoiding for the most part structural details. These brief definitions are intended merely to give the usual significance of the term in comparative vertebrate anatomy.

Abdomen. The portion of the body cavity containing most of the viscera; in mammals, the part posterior to the diaphragm.

Abduction. Movement away from the midplane of the body.

Aboral. Away from the mouth.

Acoelous (syn., *amphiplatyan*). Without a cavity; specifically, a vertebra having the centrum flat at both ends.

Acoustic. (syn., *auditory*). Pertaining to the ear or to hearing.

Acrania. Lacking a braincase; the protochordates.

Acrodont. A type of tooth attachment in which the teeth are fused to the margin of the jaw.

Adduction. Movement toward the midline of the body.

Adipose tissue. Loosely organized connective tissue containing fat cells.

Afferent. Leading to or toward the organ of reference.

Alecithal. Without yolk.

Alimentary. Pertaining to digestion or to the digestive tract.

Allantois. An embryonic respiratory and excretory organ in the amniotes.

Alveolus. A small outpocketing.

Amnion. A membrane surrounding the embryo of reptiles, birds, and mammals.

Amniote. An animal possessing an amnion; a reptile, bird, or mammal.

Amphicoelous. Having a concavity at each end; specifically, a vertebra with the centrum concave at both ends.

Amphiplatyan. See *acoelous.*

Ampulla. A small, flask-shaped cavity.

Analogy. Superficial resemblance resulting from similarity of function. (See *homology.*)

Anamniote. A vertebrate lacking an amnion; a fish or amphibian.

Anastomosis. A joining of vessels, nerves, or other structures.

Ankylosis. A fusion of a joint through bone deposition.

Anlage (syn., *primordium*). The first embryonic indication of a structure.

Anterior. Toward the head.

Anus. The posterior opening of the alimentary canal.

Aorta, dorsal. A main artery formed by the junction of the aortic arches.

Aorta, ventral (syn., *truncus arteriosus*). The main artery carrying blood from the heart.

Aortic arches. A series of paired arteries passing through the visceral arches and connecting the ventral aorta with the dorsal aorta.

Apocrine. Pertaining to glands in which the cells are partially disintegrated in the process of secretion.

Aponeurosis. A tendinous sheath or a layer of fascia serving as a muscle attachment.

Apophysis. A process or outgrowth, especially of a bone.

Appendicular skeleton. The part of the skeleton comprising the girdles and limbs.

Arachnoid. A delicate, spiderweb-like network.

Arboreal. Tree-dwelling.

Archenteron. The original embryonic gut formed of the inner germ layer of the gastrula.

Archinephros. The primitive excretory organ of the vertebrates.

Arcualia. Paired cartilages formed in sclerotomes about the notochord and the nerve cord; they give rise to the vertebrae.

Artery. A vessel that carries blood away from the heart.

Articulation. The point of juncture of two skeletal elements.

Atrium. A chamber of the heart which receives blood from the veins.

Auditory. See *acoustic.*

Autonomic nervous system. A specialized part of the peripheral nervous system that consists of nerves and ganglia and is concerned with involuntary actions.

Autostylic. Designating the method by which the upper jaw is attached to the cranium by a process from the palatoquadrate, the hyomandibular taking no part.

Axial skeleton. That part of the skeleton comprising the skull, the vertebrae, and, when present, the ribs, the sternum, and the branchial skeleton.

Axis. (1) An imaginary straight line passing through the body, used in defining anatomical planes and directions. (2) The modified second cervical vertebra of the amniotes.

Axon. The process of a neuron that carries impulses away from the cell body.

Bilateral symmetry. A type of symmetry in which one side of the body is the mirror image of the other.

Bipedal. Walking on the hind legs.

Bladder. A sac or a vesicle.

Blastocoele (syn., *segmentation cavity*). The cavity of the blastula.

Blastomere. One of the cells formed in the primary divisions of an egg.

Blastopore. The opening in a gastrula that leads to the cavity of the archenteron.

Blastula. An early stage of embryonic growth in which the cells are arranged in a sphere.

Bowman's capsule. The expanded end of a uriniferous tubule that surrounds a glomerulus.

Brachial. Referring to the anterior (pectoral) appendage.

Branchial. Referring to the gills.

Buccal. Pertaining to the mouth.

Bulbus arteriosus. An expanded portion of the proximal end of the ventral aorta.

Bursa. A saclike cavity filled with fluid, particularly one around a joint.

Caecum (pl., *caeca*). A blind pouch or saclike diverticulum.

Calcareous. Pertaining to lime salts or to deposits of calcium.

Capillary. A small, thin-walled blood vessel through which diffusion may readily take place.

Cardiac. Referring to the heart.

Carnivorous. Flesh-eating.

Carpus. The wrist.

Cartilage. A sustentative tissue with an abundant, solidified matrix; cells are round or ovoid and lack processes.

Caudal. Pertaining to the tail.

Cauda equina. The bundle of the more posterior spinal nerves which descend for a distance through the spinal canal from their point of attachment to the cord to their site of emergence between the vertebrae. (Literally, "horse's tail.")

Centrum (pl., *centra*). The body of a vertebra.

Cephalic. Pertaining to the head.

Cervical. Pertaining to the neck.

Cervix. A constricted part of an organ, e.g., the cervix of the uterus.

Chiasma. A crossing of fibers; specifically, the crossing of the optic nerves in the brain.

Chondral bone. A bone preformed in cartilage.

Chondro-. Pertaining to cartilage.

Chorion. The outer, protective membrane of the amniote embryo.

Choroid. A delicate, vascular membrane as in the choroid coat of the eye or the choroid plexus of the brain.

Cilia. Hairlike, motile cell processes.

Cloaca. A common chamber into which the urogenital tracts and the digestive tract open.

Coeliac. Pertaining to the abdominal cavity.

Coelom. The body cavity; a large, mesoderm-lined space in which the viscera lie.

Commissure. A crossing of nerve fiber tracts which connect similar parts on opposite sides of the brain or spinal cord.

Condyle. A rounded, articular facet of a bone.

Connective tissue. A sustentative tissue in which the matrix is composed largely of fibers.

Conus arteriosus. An accessory chamber of the heart between the ventricle and the ventral aorta.

Cornu. A hornlike projection.

Cortex. The outer layer of an organ.

Cosmine. A layer of dentine covering the scales of crossopterygian and dipnoan fishes.

Costal. Pertaining to ribs.

Craniata. Animals possessing a brain case; the vertebrates.

Cranium. The portion of the skull that encloses the brain.

Ctenoid. A type of scale having comblike processes on the free edge.

Cutaneous. Pertaining to the skin.

Cuvierian ducts. A pair of vessels, formed by the union of the anterior and posterior cardinal veins, which empty their blood into the sinus venosus.

Cycloid. A type of scale having a rounded free edge.

Cystic. Pertaining to a bladder, particularly to the gall bladder.

Dactyl-. Combining form denoting a digit.

Dendrite. A process of a neuron that carries impulses toward the cell body.

Dentine. A hard, dense substance found in teeth and placoid and cosmoid scales.

Dermal bone (syn., *membrane bone*). Bone originating in relation to the dermis, not preformed in cartilage.

Dermatome. The dorsolateral division of an embryonic mesodermal somite which gives rise to the dermis.

Dermis. The underlying layer of the skin.

Diaphysis. The main part of the shaft of a long bone.

Diapophysis. A transverse process of a vertebra.

Diarthrosis. A movable joint.

Diastema. A gap; specifically, a space in the jaw without teeth.

Diencephalon. The "tween brain," the division of the forebrain between the telencephalon and the mesencephalon.

Digestion. Chemical breaking up of food preparatory to its absorption and assimilation.

Digit. One of the terminal divisions of a tetrapod appendage; a finger or toe.

Diphyodont. Having two successive sets of teeth during life.

Distal. Away from the central part or point of origin.

Diverticulum. A pouch arising from a hollow organ.

Dura mater. The tough outer meningeal membrane covering the brain and spinal cord.

Ecdysis. Shedding of the outer layer of the epidermis.

Ectoderm. The outer embryonic germ layer.

Ectothermic. Depending on the absorption of environmental heat to elevate the body temperature.

Effector. A muscle or gland cell which responds to a nerve impulse, or the nerve end organ by which the impulse is transmitted to the muscle or gland.

Efferent. Leading away from; vessels, ducts, or nerves conveying blood, secretions, or nerve impulses away from a part.

Enamel. A white, hard substance that covers the dentine of a tooth.

Endocardium. The endothelial lining of the heart.

Endocrine. Pertaining to a gland whose secretion is discharged directly into the bloodstream rather than into a duct.

Endoderm. The innermost embryonic germ layer.

Endorachis. The membrane lining the cranium and spinal canal.

Endoskeleton. An internal supporting structure.

Endothelium. The inner epithelial lining of the vascular system.

Endothermic. Maintaining the body temperature through internal heat produced by metabolic activity.

Enteron. The gut.

Epaxial. Above an axis; denoting structures dorsal to the lateral septum that separates the dorsal and ventral masses of myotomal muscles.

Ependyma. The layer lining the central canal of the spinal cord and the ventricles of the brain.

Epi-. A prefix meaning "upon," or "on the outside."

Epiblast. The outer layer of the gastrula.

Epicardium. The membrane covering the surface of the heart.

Epidermis. The outer, non-vascular layer of the skin.

Epimere. The dorsal primary division of the mesoderm.

Epiphysis. (1) The pineal body. (2) Part of a long bone or vertebral centrum that ossifies separately and later fuses with the main structure.

Epithelium. A tissue that covers a surface or lines a cavity.

Evagination. An outpocketing.

Exocrine. A gland that discharges its product through a duct.

Exoskeleton. External skeletal structures, such as dermal scales.

Extension. Movement to bring the parts of a joint into or toward a straight line.

Facet. A small, articulating surface or face.

Fascia. A connective tissue sheet covering a muscle or other surface.

Fenestra. An opening within a bone or between bones. (Literally, "window.")

Fissure. A cleft or a groove.

Flexion. Movement to bend the parts of a joint.

Follicle. A small sac.

Foramen (pl., *foramina*). An opening, especially one into or through a bone.

Forebrain (syn., *prosencephalon*). The anterior part of the embryonic brain.

Fundus. The bottom or base of the internal surface of a hollow structure, e. g., of the eye, the stomach.

Ganglion. A collection of nerve cell bodies outside the central nervous system.

Ganoid. A type of scale covered with a hard, translucent material (ganoin).

Gastralia. Abdominal ribs.

Gastric. Pertaining to the stomach.

Gastrocoele. The cavity of the archenteron.

Gastrula. The embryonic stage (succeeding the blastula) in which epiblast and hypoblast become differentiated.

Germ Layer. One of the primary cell layers of the early embryo.

Gill. A vascular structure for aquatic respiration borne on a visceral arch.

Gland. An organ or a cell that secretes a specific product.

Glomerulus. A rounded mass of arterial capillaries; specifically, those in the kidney from which waste products are excreted.

Glosso-. Pertaining to the tongue.

Gonad. A primary sex organ, producing reproductive cells; the ovary or the testis.

Gyrus. A fold on the surface of the brain.

Hemal (or haemal). Pertaining to the blood.

Hemal arch. An arch of cartilage or bone extending ventrally from the centrum of a caudal vertebra to surround the caudal blood vessels.

Hemibranch. Gill filaments borne on one side of a visceral arch.

Hepatic. Pertaining to the liver.

Herbivorous. Plant-eating.

Heterodont. Having differentiated teeth.

Hilum (or hilus). A depression in an organ where vessels or nerves enter.

Hindbrain (syn., *rhombencephalon*). The posterior part of the embryonic brain.

Holoblastic. A type of cleavage in which the entire egg undergoes segmentation.

Holobranch. Two hemibranchs enclosing a visceral arch.

Holocrine. Pertaining to glands in which the cells disintegrate and are discharged along with their secretion.

Homodont. Having one type of tooth throughout.

Homoiothermic. Maintaining a constant body temperature.

Homolecithal (syn., *isolecithal*). Having the yolk distributed evenly throughout the egg.

Homology. Structural similarity based on common origin. (See *analogy.*)

Hyostylic. A type of jaw suspension in which the hyomandibular unites the jaw with the skull.

Hypaxial. Ventral to the lateral septum. (See *epaxial.*)

Hypo-. Prefix meaning "below."

Hypoblast. The inner layer of the gastrula before the mesoderm and notochord differentiate.

Hypomere. The ventral primary division of the mesoderm.

Infundibulum. A funnel; specifically, (1) the opening of the oviduct near the ovary, or (2) the evagination from the brain that gives rise to part of the pituitary gland.

Inguinal. Pertaining to the groin.

Insectivorous. Insect-eating.

Integument. The skin and its appendages.

Invagination. A term denoting a pushing in, or an ingrowth, of a part.

Isolecithal. See *homolecithal.*

Iter. A passage or an opening, specifically that between the ventricles of the brain.

Jacobson's organ. A specialized olfactory area in the nasal cavity; the vomeronasal organ.

Joint. An articulation.

Jugular. Pertaining to the neck.

Labyrinth. Intercommunicating channels, particularly the canals of the inner ear.

Lacuna. A small hollow or depression.

Lamella. A thin plate.

Larva. An immature animal that differs structurally from the adult.

Lateral line system. A series of sense organs borne in grooves or closed canals on the head and along the sides of the body of the fishlike vertebrates.

Levator. A muscle that lifts a part.

Ligament. A fibrous tissue or band that ties bones together or supports a visceral organ.

Lingual. Pertaining to the tongue.

Lumbar. Pertaining to the lower part of the back.

Lumen (pl., *lumina*). The channel or hollow center of a tube or an organ.

Lymph. The fluid in the lymphatic vessels, consisting of plasma and white blood cells.

Malar. Relating to the cheek.

Malpighian corpuscle (syn., *renal corpuscle*). The primary excretory unit consisting of a Bowman's capsule and a glomerulus.

Mandible. The lower jaw.

Manus. The hand.

Matrix. Intercellular substance of a tissue.

Maxilla. The upper jaw.

Meatus. A channel or passageway.

Medulla. The marrow; the central portion of an organ, as of the adrenal gland or kidney.

Medullated. Covered with a myelin sheath (in reference to a nerve fiber).

Meiolecithal (syn., *oligolecithal*). Pertaining to an ovum having a small amount of yolk.

Membrane. A thin layer of tissue that covers a surface or divides a space or organ.

Membrane bone. See *dermal bone.*

Meninx (pl. *meninges*). One of the membranes enveloping the brain and spinal cord.

Mental. (1) Pertaining to the mind. (2) Pertaining to the chin.

Meroblastic. A type of cleavage in which only that part of the ovum which is in the region of the animal pole divides.

Merocrine. Pertaining to glands in which the cells are neither destroyed nor injured in the process of secretion.

Mesencephalon. The middle division of the embryonic brain; the midbrain.

Mesenchyme. Loosely organized, embryonic tissue.

Mesentery. A thin sheet of tissue by which an organ is suspended in a body cavity.

Mesodaeum. The part of the embryonic gut that is lined with endoderm.

Mesoderm. The middle embryonic germ layer.

Mesodermal somite. A metameric division of the epimere.

Mesolecithal. Pertaining to an ovum having a moderate amount of yolk.

Mesomere. A primary division of the embryonic mesoderm which gives rise to the urogenital organs and ducts.

Mesonephros. A kidney structure developed from the middle part of the archinephros, serving as the embryonic kidney of the amniotes (sometimes used as a synonym of *opisthonephros*).

Mesothelium. The mesodermal lining of the body cavity.

Metamerism. The repetition of similar body segments along the axis of an animal.

Metamorphosis. Structural transformation of an animal, particularly that which takes place when the animal passes from the larval to the adult stage.

Metanephros. A kidney structure developed from the posterior part of the archinephros; the functional adult kidney of the amniotes.

Metencephalon. The anterior division of the hindbrain.

Midbrain (syn., *mesencephalon*). The middle portion of the embryonic brain.

Monophyodont. Having a single set of teeth which are not replaced.

Morphology. The study of the form and structure of plants or animals.

Myelencephalon. The posterior division of the hindbrain.

Myelin sheath. A covering surrounding the axons of some neurons.

Myelon. The spinal cord.

Myocomma (pl., *myocommata;* syn., *myoseptum*). The connective tissue septum between two myotomes.

Myoseptum. See *myocomma.*

Myotome. The median part of the mesodermal somite; gives rise to the skeletal muscles.

Naris (pl., *nares*). The nostril.

Neoteny. Retention of larval characters in the adult as a result of environmental factors.

Nephri-. Combining form referring to the kidney.

Neural. Pertaining to the nervous system.

Neurectoderm. The division of the epiblast that gives rise to the nervous system.

Neurocranium. The part of the skull that surrounds the brain.

Neuroglia. Supporting cells of the nervous system.

Notochord. The primitive or embryonic supporting column of the Chordata.

Nucleus. (1) The part of the cell that contains the chromosomes. (2) An aggregate of nerve cell bodies within the brain or spinal cord.

Occipital. Pertaining to the back part of the skull.

Ocular. Pertaining to the eye.

Olfactory. Pertaining to the sense of smell.

Oligolecithal. See *meiolecithal*.

Omnivorous. Eating both plant and animal food.

Ontogeny. The development of an individual.

Opisthocoelous. Concave behind; specifically, a vertebra with the centrum convex anteriorly and concave posteriorly.

Opisthonephros. Kidney structure developed from the middle and posterior parts of the archinephros; the functional adult kidney of most anamniotes.

Opisthotic. Pertaining to skeletal elements posterior to the ear.

Optic. Pertaining to the eye.

Oral. Referring to the mouth.

Orbit. The eye socket.

Os. (1) A bone. (2) A mouth or opening.

Osculum. A small opening.

Osteoblast. A bone-forming cell.

Osteoclast. A bone-absorbing cell.

Otic. Pertaining to the ear.

Oviparous. Type of reproduction in which the young hatch from eggs outside the mother's body.

Ovoviviparous. Type of reproduction in which the eggs are retained in the oviduct during the developmental period.

Ovum (pl., *ova*). Egg.

Paedogenesis. Genetically fixed retention of larval characters in the adult stage.

Paleontology. The study of fossil life.

Parasympathetic. The craniosacral division of the autonomic nervous system.

Pectoral. Pertaining to the chest region, the anterior girdle, and the anterior appendages.

Peduncle. A stem or supporting structure.

Pelvic. Pertaining to the posterior girdle and appendages.

Pentadactyl. Having five digits, referring to the basic pattern of the tetrapod limb.

Peri-. Prefix meaning "around."

Perichondrium. The fibrous membrane surrounding cartilage.

Periosteum. The fibrous membrane surrounding bone.

Peristalsis. The contraction wave of the intestine.

Peritoneum. The membrane that lines the abdominal cavity and encloses the visceral organs.

Pes. The foot.

Pharyngeal arches. See *visceral arches.*

Pharynx. The first part of the endodermal portion of the alimentary tract.

Phylogeny. The evolutionary history of a group of organisms.

Placoid scale. A type of dermal scale present in elasmobranchs.

Plantar. Pertaining to the sole of the foot.

Plasma. The fluid part of the blood.

Pleurodont. A type of tooth attachment in which the teeth are fused to the inner side of the jaw.

Pleuroperitoneal. Pertaining to the body space or its lining in animals that lack a diaphragm.

Plexus. A network of blood vessels or of nerves.

Poikilothermic. Having a variable body temperature.

Polylecithal. Having a large amount of yolk.

Polyphyodont. Having the teeth replaced an indefinite number of times.

Portal system. A system of veins that break up into capillaries in a specific organ.

Posterior. Away from the head.

Prehensile. Adapted for grasping and seizing.

Primordium. See *anlage.*

Process. An extension or an outgrowth.

Procoelous. Concave anteriorly; specifically, a type of vertebra with the centrum concave anteriorly and convex posteriorly.

Proctodaeum. The ectoderm-lined, posterior (anal) portion of the embryonic gut.

Pronation. Movement of a hand to a palm downward position or a similar movement of a foot.

Pronephros. The kidney derived from the anterior part of the archinephros; functional in the adult hagfish, in some teleosts, and in the embryos and larvae of other anamniotes.

Prosencephalon. The most anterior embryonic division of the brain; the forebrain.

Proximal. Nearest to the point of origin.

Pterygium. A little wing; used in connection with fin and bone terminology.

Pulmonary. Pertaining to the lungs.

Quadrupedal. Walking on four legs.

Ramus (pl., *rami*). A branch of a vessel, nerve, or bone.

Ray. A delicate, rodlike supporting structure.

Receptor. A sensory nerve cell or a sensory organ.

Renal. Pertaining to the kidney.

Renal corpuscle. See *Malpighian corpuscle.*

Rete mirabile. A plexus of capillary-sized vessels interposed within an artery or vein, as in the glomerulus of the kidney.

Rhinal. Pertaining to the nose.

Rhombencephalon. The most posterior portion of the embryonic brain; the hindbrain.

Rhombo-. A prefix denoting a parallelogram or kite-shaped figure.

Rostrum. A beaklike structure or process.

Rudimentary. Partly developed.

Sacral. Pertaining to the vertebra or vertebrae with which the pelvic girdle articulates.

Sagittal. Referring to a plane passing longitudinally through the body, dividing it into right and left parts.

Sclerotome. The mid-ventral portion of a mesodermal somite from which the axial skeleton is formed.

Sebaceous gland. A gland that secretes an oily substance (sebum).

Segmental. Pertaining to serially repeated structures.

Segmentation cavity. See *blastocoele.*

Semilunar. Half-moon shaped, as the valves in veins and in the conus arteriosus.

Septum (pl., *septa*). A wall or partition.

Sinus. A hollow space, as in a bone or in the vascular system.

Sinus venosus. An accessory chamber of the heart into which the veins empty (in fishes, amphibians, and some reptiles).

Somatic. (1) Pertaining to parts of the body external to the coelom, in contrast to *visceral*, which applies to parts within the coelom. (2) In the nervous system, relating to fibers that innervate the external sense organs and voluntary muscles, in contrast to *visceral fibers* which innervate the viscera, glands, and involuntary muscles. (3) Relating to general body cells in contrast to germ cells.

Somatic hypomere. The layer of hypomere external to the coelom.

Somatopleure. The somatic hypomere and its surrounding ectoderm.

Somite. A metameric division of the epimeric mesoderm.

Sphincter. An annular muscle surrounding and constricting an opening.

Spine. (1) A pointed process of a bone. (2) The backbone.

Splanchnic. Relating to the viscera.

Splanchnic hypomere. The layer of hypomere internal to the coelom.

Splanchnocranium. The part of the skull derived from the visceral skeleton.

Splanchnopleure. The splanchnic hypomere and adjoining endoderm.

Stomodaeum. The ectoderm-lined, anterior (oral) end of the embryonic gut.

Stratum corneum. The outer layer of dead cells in the skin of a tetrapod.

Subclavian. Below the clavicle, referring to structures in the shoulder region.

Sulcus. A furrow; a shallow groove in the surface of the brain.

Supination. Turning the palm of the hand upward or a similar movement of a foot.

Supine. Lying on the back.

Suspensory ligament. A ligament that holds up a part.

Sustentative tissue. A tissue in which the cells are inclosed in an abundant matrix.

Suture. A line of junction of neighboring bones.

Symphysis. A line of fusion between bones that were originally separate.

Sympathetic System. The thoracolumbar division of the autonomic nervous system.

Syn-. A prefix denoting a union.

Synarthrosis. An immovable joint; a suture.

System. A group of organs that serve a common function.

Systemic. Pertaining to the body as a whole, as in systemic circulation (as opposed to pulmonary circulation).

Telencephalon. The anterior division of the forebrain.

Telolecithal. Having the yolk concentrated in one hemisphere of the ovum.

Tendon. A cord of fibrous connective tissue by which a muscle is attached to a bone or other structure.

Tetrapod. Having four appendages based on the pentadactyl plan; an amphibian, a reptile, a bird, or a mammal.

Thecodont. A type of tooth attachment in which the teeth are set in sockets in the jawbone.

Trema-. A combining form denoting an opening.

Truncus arteriosus. See *aorta, ventral*.

Tunic. A coat; one of the layers of tissue of which various organs are comprised, as the tunics of the eyeball or of a blood vessel.

Unguis. The non-living, corneous layer of a nail, hoof, or claw.

Ur-, Urino-, Uro-. Prefixes denoting the excretory system.

Uro-. Prefix denoting the tail.

Vas. A vessel or duct.

Vasomotor. Relating to nerves that act upon blood vessels.

Vein. A vessel conveying blood toward the heart.

Vent. An opening; specifically, the opening of the cloaca to the outside.

Venter. The belly surface.

Ventral. The abdominal side.

Ventricle. A small cavity, especially one in the brain; a chamber of the heart.

Vertebra. One of the skeletal segments of the spinal column.

Vesicle. A small sac or a bladder.

Vestigial. The more or less reduced remains of a structure that has losts its ancestral function.

Viscera (sing., *viscus*). The soft internal organs.

Visceral arches (syn., *pharyngeal arches*). Columns of tissue, supported by cartilaginous or bony rods, that bound the visceral pouches.

Visceral pouches (syn., *pharyngeal pouches*). Paired pouches that arise from the walls of the embryonic pharynx.

Visceral skeleton. Skeletal parts developed in connection with the visceral arches.

Viviparous. Type of reproduction in which the young develop in the uterus of the female and receive nourishment from the maternal blood stream.

Yolk. Nutritive material contained within the ovum.

Zygo-. A combining term denoting a yoke or a pair.

Zygote. The fertilized egg.

Index

A number in boldface indicates a page containing an illustration.

231

Vestibule, 103
Visceral arches, 38, **97**
Visceral cartilages, 58
Visceral clefts, **97**
Visceral furrows, 96, **97**
Visceral motor nerves, 195
Visceral muscles, 81
Visceral nerves, 176
Visceral peritoneum, **5,** 86
Visceral pouches, 96, **97**
Visceral ramus, 165
Visceral sensory nerves, 165
Visceral slits, 38
Vitelline veins, 131, 142
Vitreous humor, 181
Vocal cords, 102
Vocal sacs, 102
Voice box, 102
Vomeronasal organ, 195

Vomers, 60

Water cells, 91
Wax glands, 49
Weberian ossicles, 188
Wharton's duct, 87
White matter, 153
    in spinal cord, 163–164
White ramus, 174
White roe, 124
Wolffian duct, 114

Yolk sac, 40, 107
Ypsiloid cartilage, 73

Zygantrum, 69
Zygomatic arch, 62
Zygosphene, 69